• HALSGROVE DISCOVER SERIES ➤

The Mining Heritage of
CORNWALL
and WEST DEVON

• HALSGROVE DISCOVER SERIES ➤

The Mining Heritage of
CORNWALL
and WEST DEVON

A GUIDE TO THE REGION'S WORLD HERITAGE SITE

PETER HANCOCK

HALSGROVE

First published in Great Britain in 2008

British Library Cataloguing-in-Publication Data
A CIP record for this title is available from the British Library

ISBN 978 1 84114 753 6

HALSGROVE
Halsgrove House, Ryelands Industrial Estate,
Bagley Road, Wellington, Somerset TA21 9PZ
Tel: 01823 653777   Fax: 01823 216796
email: sales@halsgrove.com
website: www.halsgrove.com

Printed and bound by D'Auria Industrie Grafiche, Italy

Contents

INTRODUCTION

In July 2006 Cornwall and West Devon Mining Landscape became a World Heritage Site, placing ten distinct areas of the South West alongside the 812 that exist world-wide, including the Pyramids of Egypt, the Taj Mahal and the Great Barrier Reef. World Heritage Sites can be found in 137 countries, and are divided into 628 cultural sites, 160 natural ones and 24 mixed properties.

The submission was presented to The United Nations Educational, Scientific and Cultural Organisation's (UNESCO) World Heritage Committee at Vilnius, Lithuania, by the Secretary of State for Culture, Media and Sport on behalf of the Cornish Mining World Heritage team. Its acceptance was the culmination of years of work by individuals and over seventy organisations who were responsible for putting together the bid.

In May 2007 a small inscription ceremony, attended by Prince Charles, took place at Cotehele House to celebrate the achievement. This marked the official designation and acknowledged the contribution the region made to the Industrial Revolution, both in Britain as well as around the world. As Prince Charles said in his speech, "Cornish hard rock expertise shaped the mining world in a dynamic way".

So what does it mean for the areas concerned, and Cornwall and West Devon in general?

- The sites that have been identified by the designation should be protected and preserved for posterity.

- It should bring about greater investment in our heritage sites, such as the £6 million spent on the Tamar Valley Mining Heritage Project to open up fresh areas of the Tamar Valley to the public.

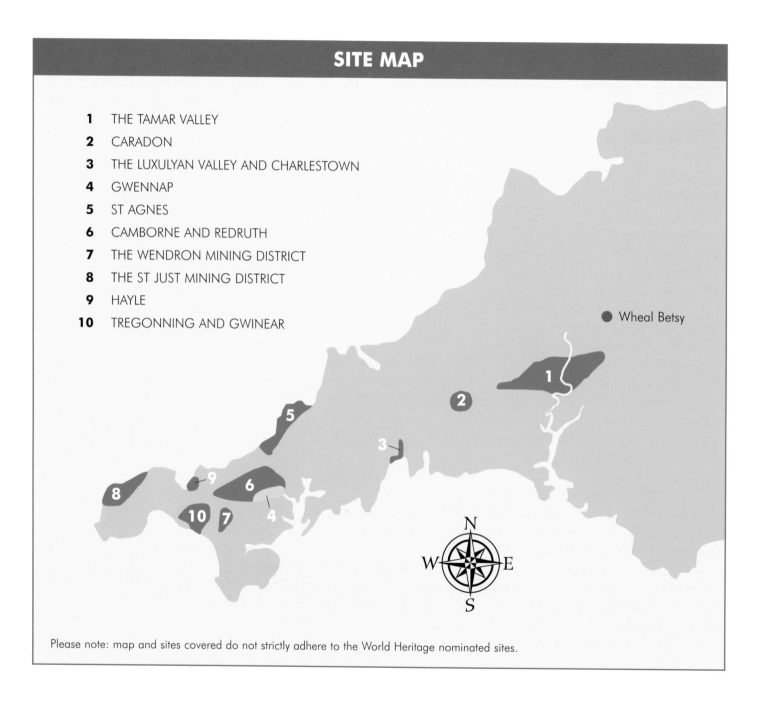

SITE MAP

1 THE TAMAR VALLEY
2 CARADON
3 THE LUXULYAN VALLEY AND CHARLESTOWN
4 GWENNAP
5 ST AGNES
6 CAMBORNE AND REDRUTH
7 THE WENDRON MINING DISTRICT
8 THE ST JUST MINING DISTRICT
9 HAYLE
10 TREGONNING AND GWINEAR

Wheal Betsy

Please note: map and sites covered do not strictly adhere to the World Heritage nominated sites.

- It will therefore provide greater access to the sites.

- Improved information boards and visual interpretation equipment should be made available.

- The sites will provide a fresh focus for visitors.

Mines did not deal exclusively in just one commodity; it depended on what mineral was found and the price of ore at a given time. Tin was often at a greater depth than copper, for example. Thus, depending on the location, tin, copper, arsenic, lead, iron, granite and later china clay could be sought. The region possessed a wide range of minerals, but no coal, so the bulk of the ore was sent to smelters in South Wales. It was convenient and cost-effective to send out ore from local ports, then return with coal. Timber, bricks, lime and machinery were also required.

Usually the first strikes were the most profitable, the ore being relatively easily won from close to the surface and without the need for much drainage, such as highly successful strikes at Wheal Virgin in Gwennap in 1757, or Wheal Maria north of Gunnislake in 1844. Once copper was exhausted a mine might survive by turning to arsenic, either from continued mining or working over previously discarded deposits, as happened at Kelly Bray Mine. Some concentrated on silver and lead, such as the Menheniot mines, or iron ore like Restormel Royal Iron Mine near Lostwithiel, at one time the largest iron mine in Cornwall.

It is worth considering the structure of employment and the terminology used in most mines in the South-West. The landowners granted the right to speculators or 'adventurers' to mine on their land, for which they gained a share of the profits. The adventurers took the risks. The cost book system was generally adopted whereby adventurers took out shares in multiples of eight (Just 8, commonly 64, or even 1024). All profits were paid as dividends and divided between them, a system that left no reserves to see them over hard times or for investment. The ore was sold at regular 'ticketings' a form of auction where smelters' agents attached to samples of ore tickets on which was stated the price they were willing to pay. These were subject to the vagaries of fluctuating world prices. Similarly miners' rates of pay were negotiated with the head of the mine, the 'captain', before a job was undertaken, and went to the team or 'pair' who were the lowest bidder. Tut-workers were paid so much a fathom of tunnel driven, while the more skilled tributers were paid according to the value of the ore they brought to the surface. Their tools were provided by the mine, but it was the miners' responsibility to maintain them. Materials required, such as candles, gunpowder and fuses, were charged against the miners' accounts, at a profit to the adventurers. Thus they often used as little as possible, to the detriment of their own safety. So at every level there was a desire for a mine to be successful.

It has to be remembered that today virtually every location mentioned here is but a shadow of its former self. Even though the focus of mining activity soon after an initial strike was below ground, it still required extensive surface workings, with water wheels, engine houses and headframes to operate pumps and lifts, as well as dressing floors, storage areas, and large dumps for the 'deads'. Often miles of leats provided water, tram tracks snaked through the workings, while lines of flat-rods oscillated across the ground to operate pumps at various shafts. Then there were ancillary buildings like workshops, stables, a count house, sawmills, stores and miners' quarters.

If a mine proved successful other adventurers soon gained the rights to work neighbouring setts. Sometimes they were equally successful, at other times, after investing a great deal of money in a venture they came away with nothing.

In more intensive mining areas, such as at Camborne/Redruth, Caradon or Devon Great Consols, it must have been like a scene from Dante's *Inferno*; the fiery glow from boilers and noise from all quarters: surface workers, often bal-maidens and children, sorting through the rock, pounding stamps breaking it even smaller, whirring headgear and machinery, and the background tinkle of running water, channelled through sluices to settling tanks or to drive water wheels, or running to waste having been brought from deep below ground.

The whole landscape was transformed into an industrial wasteland, and very different to what we see today. It is a far cry from our romantic image of these places, and it is a testimony to Mother Nature that they have recovered so well.

Today the visitor can easily be misled by the conflicting evidence before them, for ironically, little remains of some of the largest mines, whilst occasional predominant engine
houses stand as silent sentinels to less successful or more recent ventures.

Public access and rights of way to the individual sites varies considerably. Some
sites – not necessarily the most important in their day – have well established visitor
centres, others are unmarked and are only sought out by the more inquisitive and tena-
cious. These, using a modicum of imagination, can be the most rewarding. However, it
is not wise to venture from a well-worn path for fear of encountering a hidden shaft.

Throughout the text map references are based on Ordnance Survey 1:25,000 scale
Explorer Maps. Whilst locations are provided, public rights of way should be deter-
mined.

THE TAMAR VALLEY

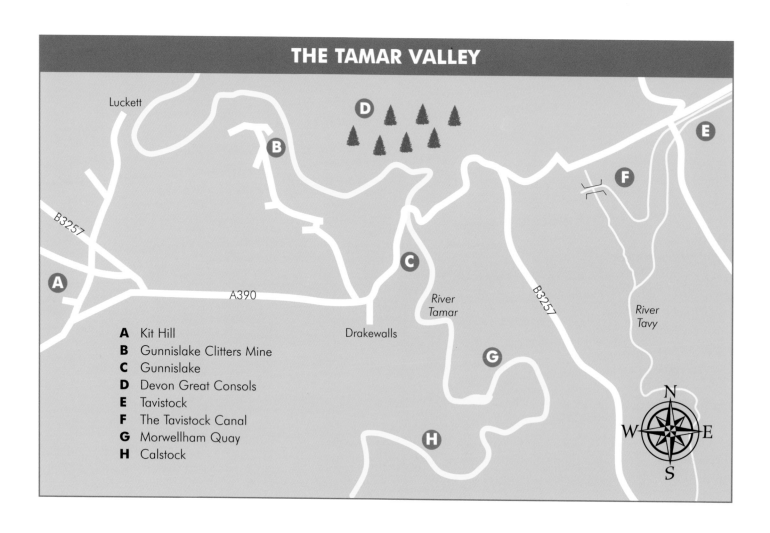

Luckett

B3257

A390

Drakewalls

River
Tamar

River
Tavy

B3257

A Kit Hill
B Gunnislake Clitters Mine
C Gunnislake
D Devon Great Consols
E Tavistock
F The Tavistock Canal
G Morwellham Quay
H Calstock

Chapter 1
THE TAMAR VALLEY

Straddling the Devon/Cornwall border, the valley contains Gunnislake, Morwellham Quay and Calstock. There were over 100 mines in this area during the nineteenth century.

A. KIT HILL (Map 108 - 374716)

Dominating the skyline of east Cornwall is the 25 metre tall chimney stack on the summit of Kit Hill, itself 333 metres above sea level. Originally Duchy of Cornwall land, it was given to Cornwall County Council to celebrate the birth of Prince William, and there is free public access and ample parking. However, apart from the stack there are few definable mine workings left today, although perhaps the panoramic views are compensation. The flat-roofed engine house that once stood next to it has disappeared, and it is hard to imagine that the original land owners who stipulated the landmark should be deliberately constructed to look like a monument would have approved of the modern aerials sprouting from it on necklace-like metal bands. Originally the stack and engine house were whitewashed to serve as a daymark for sailors.

Taking further advantage of the exposed position, the only windmill ever used to drain a mine once stood here, operating during the 1830s. The method did not prove consistent or powerful enough; even so, it was destroyed in a storm. Again nothing of it survives.

The site was worked as a wolfram and tin mine: the importance of wolfram for hardening steel ensured the establishment's survival during World War One.

Following the contours to the north of Kit Hill the East Cornwall Mineral Railway ran

Kit Hill stack. Because of its commanding vantage point, today it makes an ideal support for aerials.

One of the few surviving industrial remains at Kit Hill.

the 12 km between Kelly Bray and Calstock, with an incline used to reach the port in the valley. It was constructed between 1864 and 1872, with a gauge of 3 foot 6 inches. A further inclined tramway ran from the quarry on the northern slopes of Kit Hill, this branch line enabling granite to be transported as well as ore and coal, and complementing that carried from the Gunnislake quarries. Sidings led off the railway to the various mines along its route.

B. GUNNISLAKE CLITTERS MINE (Ref. 422720)

Approached via the road from Gunnislake to Latchley, the imposing chimney stack of Greenhill Arsenic Works can be see towards the top of the hill, the outer skin of brickwork now crumbling away while the crown is still stained white. (Ref. 418716) This operation was incorporated into Gunnislake Clitters Mine around 1880, the extensive ruins of which can be seen amongst the trees by the side of the road. The earliest documented records for this mine are from the 1820s, but evidence of earlier workings have been found. During the nineteenth century copper, tin, arsenic and wolfram were mined, but during the peak years of production between 1881 and 1883 some 2,500 tons

Gunnislake Clitters Mine.

The Mill at Gunnislake Clitters Mine c.1900.

15

An overgrown engine house at Drakewalls Mine, Gunnislake.

of copper were raised each year and the mine employed nearly 200 people. An inclined tramway connected the mine with the East Cornwall Mineral Railway further up the hillside, making redundant an earlier track that ran along the floor of the valley to the wharves at Gunnislake.

For the adventurous, a footpath leads down the hill past extensive red sand tailings to the remains of a processing mill and dressing floors near the river, as well as the mouth of the adit that once drained the mine prior to the erection of a 40 inch steam engine in 1864. As late as 1902-09 almost 550 tons of black tin and 440 tons of wolfram were produced here, and together with smaller quantities of arsenic, realised £83,000.

C. GUNNISLAKE (Ref. 433716)

Within the steep wooded valley of the River Tamar stands the fifteenth-century New Bridge, until the opening of the suspension bridge at Saltash in 1961 the lowest crossing

Preserved remains at Drakewalls, yet a fraction of this once extensive sett.

point of the river by road. When minerals were discovered in the valley the little village of Williamstown, named after the local squire, swelled, and in 1828 the settlement became Gunnislake after 'gunnis' meaning a cutting or open mine adit, of which there were soon many, for the mines could be drained into the valley. The village thrived as the mines prospered, and once had 45 shops.

The first venture in the area was Old Gunnislake Mine, while to the south at the top of the hill Drakewalls was the largest producer of tin in east Cornwall for a period during the mid-nineteenth century. Soon it would be overshadowed by the hugely successful Devon Great Consols that covered a substantial area to the north on the Devon side of the Tamar. Above Gunnislake Station a few chimney stacks and crumbling engine houses mark the sett of Drakewalls Mine. (Ref. 426706) Tin was found close to the surface so was originally worked from a deep gunnis or cutting. As the lodes were chased deeper it was drained by adits and water wheels, but later steam was adopted, both for pumping and driving stamps. After tin prices fell in the 1880s, during a period when it was known as Drakewalls United the mine turned increasingly to copper and arsenic.

In February 1889 it gained notoriety when two miners were trapped underground, but were successfully rescued after four days.

D. DEVON GREAT CONSOLS

When a number of mines were joined together, or 'consolidated', during the 1850s they became Europe's most important copper producer. They began in 1844 with Wheal Maria, a hugely rich and profitable mine named after the wife of Josiah Hitchins, the original adventurer. The following year Wheal Fanny opened, named after his daughter, as well as Wheal Anna Maria, after the Duchess of Bedford whose family owned the land. Wheal Josiah followed soon after, as well as Wheal Emma in 1848, named after the widow of a shareholder, William Morris, to which Watson's Mine was added later, taking its name from the company chairman, Peter Watson.

By 1850 these mines were employing 1,024 people, of whom 455 worked underground. They reached their apogee six years later, producing 28,836 tons of ore, the largest annual output recorded by any mine covered in this account. In 1858 a railway was built from

A view across the Tamar Valley from Gunnislake Clitters Mine towards Devon Great Consols. The extensive burrows can be seen, despite the vegetation.

18

Wheal Anna Maria where there were sidings and storage yards, via the various mines, to a point above Morwellham. There was even a small foundry, established in 1862, to manufacture equipment, augmenting that being produced by Bedford Foundry in Tavistock. Man-engines were installed at Wheal Josiah and Wheal Emma in 1865, although because of the extensive workings a system requiring a single entrance was not ideal.

The mine's fortunes declined towards the end of the nineteenth century, and it turned to arsenic before closing completely between the wars. The Duke of Bedford had stipulated in the contracts that when the mines closed the surface workings had to be cleared and conifers planted. So despite their success, today access to much of this area is very difficult, the terrain being heavily wooded and traversed by a myriad of tracks, often through private land. (Blanchdown Wood, Ref. 4273) The course of the railway remains intact, and has been opened up for walkers and cyclists. Known as the Tamar Valley Mining Heritage Project, it involved the construction in 2007 of an underpass to provide a safe crossing point of the A390 at Gulworthy.

Below left: *The waterwheel at Devon Great Consols arsenic works c.1940.* Below right: *The shaft at the Main Lode at the Bedford United Mine, showing the railway line from Devon Great Consols c.1920.*

E. TAVISTOCK

Much of Tavistock was laid out by Francis Russell, 7th Duke of Bedford (1788-1861), who also instigated the construction of the Guildhall and Bedford Cottages and miners' cottages, while his agent resided at the present Bedford Hotel on Plymouth Road. Theophilus Jones, resident architect and surveyor between 1848 and 1858, influenced many of the buildings.

To service the mines Bedford Foundry off Bannawell Street (Ref. 479747) was established in 1841. It flourished over the next few years, supplying steam engines, boilers, machinery and even a small locomotive to Devon Great Consols, and at its peak employed some ninety men. Tavy Foundry (Ref. 486746) that stood near Stannary Bridge, (formerly Mount Foundry) was run by brothers James and Henry Pearce from the 1850s to the 1930s.

Far left: Former Bedford Foundry premises, Tavistock.

Left: The site of Tavy Foundry from Stannary Bridge.

F. THE TAVISTOCK CANAL   (Ref. 483744 to 463726)

The Tavistock Canal was the work of John Taylor (1779-1863). Born in Norwich and trained as a land surveyor and civil engineer, he was appointed manager of Wheal Friendship at Mary Tavy when just nineteen. It was the start of a busy and illustrious career. His interests took him far and wide, including involvement in foreign mines, but when not travelling he spent some time in the town.

Construction of the canal took over fifteen years at an estimated cost of between £40 and

£68,000, and it was opened in 1817. At its head near the present day car park, where it was fed from the nearby River Tavy, were coal and ore wharves. Some of the wharf buildings beside the neglected canal can still be seen. It linked Tavistock with Morwellham, and included a 2.4 km-long tunnel driven beneath Morwell Down, partly built by French prisoners-of-war, and the Lumburn aqueduct, completed in August 1808, required to cross the River Lumburn some 18.3 metres below. Ore was transported downstream, while coal and limestone made the return journey, the barges being propelled through the tunnel using poles.

The once vibrant canal declined along with the fortunes of the mines, and was further precipitated by the South Devon Railway to Tavistock during the 1860s. However, it gained a new use that could never have been dreamt of by its creator, supplying water for a hydro-electric plant at Morwellham. Today the canal can be followed through 'The Meadows' park and out of the town past Fitzford Cottages (1869) (Ref. 475738) near Drake's statue. It continues past Crowndale, the great sailor's birthplace, and is accessible as far as the aqueduct where it reaches private land, but a short distance further on, near Wheal Crebor, it disappears into the tunnel.

Taylor Square, Tavistock.

The weir below Abbey Bridge marks the start of the Tavistock Canal.

Tavistock Canal.

Right: *A restored swing bridge and lock gate on the canal.*

Far right: *Tavistock Canal, the sylvan setting belying its industrial past.*

22

G. MORWELLHAM QUAY (Ref. 445696)

A former copper port, today it is run by the Morwellham and Tamar Valley Trust and is a popular heritage site and tourist destination.

To connect the Tavistock Canal with the wharves at river level 72 metres below in the valley, a 220 metre long, 1 in 6 inclined plane was constructed. It is likely that John Taylor originally planned a series of locks, but with the project running at 50% over-budget a cheaper solution had to be found. There were a pair of tracks, the iron canal barges carried on trolleys hauled by a waterwheel as well as being counterbalanced. Water from the canal was also used to power a range of machinery at the port. Towards the bottom of the incline one track led off to Bath's Quay near George and Charlotte Mine while the other descended directly to the wharves in the village. Over the years a variety of rail profiles were tried, as well as sleepers of granite and later the slate that can be seen today.

Morwellham Quay.

After The South Devon Railway was built between 1857-58 the canal was past its heyday. The railway arrived above the port from the mines of Devon Great Consols some 7 km away, and was connected to the storage floors by an incline operated by a 22-inch winding engine. The Great Dock was built between 1856 and 1858 on former water meadows. To reach this new facility a tunnel was cut beneath the timber yard (now the village green) and a row of cottages. This has recently been the subject of an archaeological excavation which discovered that the track was laid on large, one foot square baulks of timber, in a similar way to Brunel's broad gauge railway, yet was standard gauge here. When the rails were lifted in 1903 the tunnel and approach cutting had been filled in.

Similar large square-cut pieces of timber formed the sides of the dock basin, held in place by iron collars. Up to six vessels could be accommodated at any one time. To avoid the ore being contami-

The impressive 32 foot waterwheel at Morwellham. It came from the clay works at Heddon Down near Cornwood, Devon, to replace the original.

23

The restored Great Dock at Morwellham, showing the elevated tramways and ore floors.

The partly tiled ore floor, with a period vessel alongside.

nated whilst being stored, the quays were tiled, partly replicated today. Large quantities of timber, usually from the Baltic but also Canada, were brought in, as well as lime; the village had a small lime kiln. Constructed from large timbers, the trestle railways that carried the ore from the incline to the quays, from where it could be tipped straight on to the storage floors, have also been re-built. Remarkably, although vast quantities of ore were stored, weighed and sampled here, it was still sold at the traditional ticketings held at Truro or Redruth. The hamlet once boasted a thriving inn, as well as a chapel, offices, and workshops.

A short walk up the valley is George and Charlotte Mine. Along with William and Mary Mine, it formed Devon and Cornwall United, a small operation that mined copper from adits driven into the hillside from the early nineteenth century. A tramway now takes visitors into the mine.

H. CALSTOCK (Ref. 435687)

The twelve-arch viaduct that dominates the scene was opened in 1908 when the East Cornwall Mineral Railway was converted to standard gauge. To reach the village a 1 in

Calstock, today a sleepy village dominated by the railway viaduct.

The once vibrant quays crossed by railway tracks are today private gardens.

6 incline descended from Calstock Consols above the village, requiring a final section of wooden trestles before terminating at Kelly Quay.

During the nineteenth century Calstock was a busy port, with sea-going vessels, steam paddle tugs such as *Empress* and *Aerial*, and barges plying the river. Wharves were built where the ore could be weighed, sampled and trans-shipped, and where coal and timber could be off-loaded. Its prosperity was reflected in ancillary trades and services; at one time the main street had eleven pubs, the Commercial Hotel, three chapels, as well as the old church of St Andrew.

Today this attractive hideaway reveals little industrial legacy and the wharves that once lined the river bank have been transformed by private houses and gardens, but the course of the incline and railway can be followed up a footpath to the west of the village (It starts opposite the boatyard; map reference 430688) providing panoramic views of the river. Other wharves were built at Gawton Quay and New Quay that were also used to ship ore from Devon Great Consols as well as nearby mines. Further downstream Weir Quay served South Tamar Mine and Tamar Consols that were mainly extracting lead.

The abandoned winding engine at Wheal Friendship photographed in the mid 1930s.

Wheal Betsy pumping engine house. Previously the mine had relied on water wheels.

I. MARY TAVY (Map 112 - 503794)

Wheal Friendship operated from 1796 and was a hugely successful copper mine in its early years, with levels sunk to 170 fathoms, yet economically drained using water-wheels taking advantage of streams flowing off Dartmoor. Unusually, it also had two inclined shafts that reached deep into the mine, up which trams of ore were hauled to the surface harnessing the power of water. The mine was also the principal reason for the Tavistock Canal. As the mine struggled during the difficult 1860s it turned increasingly to mispickel (arsenical pyrite) used to make arsenic in order to survive. It continued into the mid 1920s.

Further north beside the A386 to Okehampton was the less successful Wheal Betsy, mined for lead and silver, the lead being smelted on site using locally cut peat as well as coal brought via the Tavistock Canal. The surviving engine house at Job's Shaft dates from 1868 when run as Prince Arthur Consols Lead Mine. The mine finally closed in 1877. It is now owned by the National Trust who restored it in 1967. There were several other lead and tin mines on Dartmoor.

Wheal Betsy displaying its crooked stack.

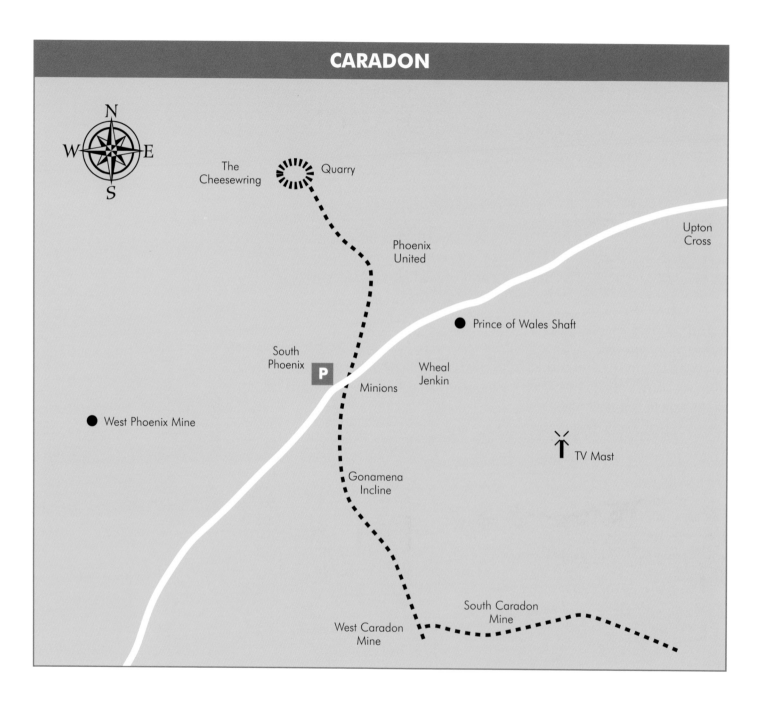

CARADON

The Cheesewring

Quarry

Phoenix United

Upton Cross

Prince of Wales Shaft

South Phoenix

P

Minions

Wheal Jenkin

West Phoenix Mine

TV Mast

Gonamena Incline

South Caradon Mine

West Caradon Mine

Chapter 2
CARADON

For over 50 years this area was the third largest producer of copper in Cornwall. A railway linked it to the port of Looe. The importance of the Caradon area may be appreciated when one considers that over 650,000 tons of copper ore was raised here between 1840 and 1887. This would be worth some £110 million in today's figures.

A. THE MINES AND VILLAGES

Despite being the third largest producer of copper in Cornwall, this windswept corner of Bodmin Moor around Caradon Hill flourished and died within half a century. Now left to sheep and walkers, the grassy pock-marked and rock-strewn hillsides reveal little of their past glory, and just a few of the once multifarious engine houses hint at the vast wealth won from beneath their foundations.

Pensilva in the early 1900s.

Tremar Coombe c.1900.

Mine captain James Clymo had previously mined for tin, but in 1837 he and his two sons discovered rich copper seams at South Caradon. The mine flourished, leading to the creation of mining communities such as Minions, Tremar, Darite and Pensilva. Originally known as Bodmonland after the local manor, with cottages springing up on Penharget Down and Silva Down the village name changed to a combination of the two. (Map 109 - 294698) Soon the settlement had three chapels, a school and village stores. Word of the area's success had attracted miners from west Cornwall where the copper reserves were declining. In 1870 the mine's engineer, William West, noted that most of the miners were western men, and he expressed the hope that they and their families would find themselves thoroughly comfortable in the east.

In the village of Luckett (Map 108 - 388737) near Kit Hill a former miners' barracks survives, though at present in a parlous state and awaiting renovation. This served the nearby New Consols mine. Known as the 'Union', the hostel was run by the Rowe family who occupied one end, while there was a large dormitory upstairs for the miners.

The road through the village of Darite c.1910.

B. SOUTH CARADON MINE (Map 109 - 266697)

During the 1860s South Caradon was expanded, with new shafts sunk, one provided with its own tramway to the dressing floors. A prosperous operation, it could indulge in drying and changing-houses for the miners, and even a barber's shop.

As it turned out, South Caradon had the last man-engine installed in Cornwall by West in 1872, for although others were contemplated or the work begun, they were never completed. By stepping on and off the rising and falling treads on the rod running down the shaft from fixed platforms the miners could progress up or down. However, this system, developed in Germany, was costly to install and plagued with accidents, so was not widely adopted. Instead ladder-roads remained common, and later skips and gigs raised by whim engines were used too.

Even after many other copper mines had closed, both around Caradon and in the west, in 1873 South Caradon still sold 5,230 tons, which was the largest amount in the county at that time. In the next ten years though the copper depression caught up with it and in 1885 operations ceased.

Today the line of the railway track can be followed along a footpath running south from Minions post office. Granite sleepers can still be found, and for the sharp-eyed, even lengths of track used for fence posts and a stile. The path runs through the old Gonamena incline (Ref. 263704) and on past mountains of mine waste left by West

South Caradon Mine; derelict engine houses amongst piles of spoil on the hillside, caught in the evening light.

The vast burrows produced by South Caradon Mine have transformed the landscape.

Man's influence on Caradon Hill is all too clear to see.

Looking across the valley from West Caradon towards South Caradon Mine. The ivy-clad engine house on the right is at Jope's Shaft which was equipped with a man-engine in about 1870.

South Caradon Mine.

The engine house and tunnel entrance to the incline at Rule's Shaft. In the opposite direction a tramway ran downhill to the dressing floors.

33

The dramatic sculptural form of the engine house at Rule's Shaft, South Caradon Mine.

Caradon Mine. In the floor of the valley parts of the cobbled dressing floors can be discerned. Here the water from the stream once powered a 30 foot water wheel.

The ochre-coloured burrows around Rule's and Kittow's Shafts can be seen for miles around. Next to the engine house at Jope's Shaft stands the overgrown ruins of the boiler house, and the walled-in shaft.

C. THE LISKEARD & CARADON RAILWAY

To link the Caradon mines and quarries with the port at Looe, in 1846 the Liskeard & Caradon Railway was opened. This carried ore and granite downhill and south to Moorswater (Map 107 - 235644) from where the canal and river were navigable. Branches ran from the granite quarry at Cheesewring (Map 109 - 258724), Kilmar Tor, Bearah Quarry and Wheal Phoenix mine. It originally needed an inclined plane at Gonamena, while another branch followed the contours to the south of the hill to service the eastern mines, with a depot at Tokenbury. The local granite was used for sleepers, whilst horses, stabled at Moorswater, provided the motive power along the standard gauge track.

This bridge carried the Cheesewring branch line that linked Gonamena and South Caradon mines with the Liskeard & Caradon Railway before the Tokenbury Branch was extended.

Houseman's Engine House, South Phoenix Mine, built in 1881 was later turned into a dwelling, as revealed by the built up bob wall and domestic chimney on the right. It now houses the small Minions Heritage Centre.

35

Granite sets remain where the railway once ran from the Cheesewring quarry, linking the adjacent mines with Moorswater and the canal to Looe.

The locomotive Caradon *which ran on the Liskeard & Caradon railway from 1862 until the closure of the line in 1917. The railway operated from the mid 1840s to serve the mines, carrying ore to the head of the Looe-Moorswater Canal.*

D. THE LISKEARD AND LOOE UNION CANAL

The Liskeard and Looe Union Canal had been open since 1828, taking the copper to wharves at Looe from where it was shipped to South Wales. This was more economical as far more fuel was required for smelting compared with the amount of ore used. Meanwhile coal, sand and timber were brought up to the mines from the coast.

In 1860 the railway was extended the whole distance to Buller Quay in Looe, making the canal redundant, with halts at Causeland and Sandplace. At its peak the line carried 45,000 tons of copper ore and coal a year. Replacing the horses, three locomotives were later introduced; *Caradon* in 1862, *Cheesewring* in 1864 and *Kilmar* in 1869.

The world slump in copper prices that led to South and East Caradon mines closing in 1885 had a knock-on effect on the railway, which went bankrupt the following year. It saw occasional use by the Great Western Railway carrying granite or serving the surviving Phoenix mines, but closed for good in 1917, and the line was subsequently dismantled.

Today parts of the various routes of the railway track can be discerned running south from Kilmar Tor, and the section to Cheesewring Quarry retains its granite sleepers. It is hard to believe the once-thriving village of Moorswater, that had a church, chapel, shop, inn and iron foundry, and was important in the commercial development of neighbouring Liskeard, is now in the path of the busy A38, whilst surviving limekilns are lost amidst an industrial estate. The lower section of the railway continues as the Looe Valley Line.

Granite sleepers remain in the bed of the old railway track leading to Cheesewring Quarry. The Prince of Wales engine house is on the right.

Above: *The route of the Liskeard & Caradon Railway can be followed in places such as this to the south of Caradon Hill.*

Left: *The route to Cheesewring Quarry.*

The Prince of Wales engine house with its distinctive chimney utilising a square base and brick stack.

E. PHOENIX UNITED (Map 109 - 265716)

Phoenix United weathered the storm for it was now producing tin, selling 600 tons in 1885, a figure only beaten by Dolcoath and East Pool. By now the combined setts covered an area of 280 hectares, chasing the lodes to the south of Cheesewring Tor. However, the following years were difficult, the mine being dogged by accidents and a slump in the price of tin. It staggered on until 1898.

The sett's landowner was the Duchy of Cornwall, and when it re-opened in 1908 with the sinking of a new shaft, it was christened the Prince of Wales Shaft by the future George V during a visit the following June. Prince Charles would also pay a visit in 1994. Yet the cost of this work, along with the increasing drainage required, exhausted the company's capital, so the last of the once great Caradon mines closed in 1914.

Today the most impressive remains - and the most recent - centre round the Prince of Wales engine house with its distinctive square base to the chimney stack. It is

The remains of the large boiler house next to the engine house on the right, with buildings that contained a two-cylinder steam winder, boiler and compressor on the left.

The Prince of Wales engine house and ancillary buildings from the tramway to Cheesewring Quarry.

Neat brick arched windows and doors are a feature of the buildings.

approached either from the track that once carried the railway to the mine, or along a public footpath from the road to Upton Cross. Abutting the engine house, which housed an 80 inch pumping engine and one of the last large Cornish engines to be built, stands the large roofless boiler house with arched brick windows. A smaller building contained a winder, boiler and compressor. Another large building stands a short distance away which housed a Robey horizontal engine to drive pneumatic stamps. The count house has been converted into a private residence.

Other engine houses, concrete foundations and embankments can be identified on the heath, providing a fragmentary picture of a once heavily industrialised scene.

F. WHEAL JENKIN (Map 109 - 265712)

Two ruined engine houses stand near the road between Minions and Caradon Hill. During the 1830s this was operated under the Cornwall Great United Mining Association that ran several mines in the area at that time, including Phoenix and Wheal

The village centre at Minions in the early 1900s.

Wheal Jenkin on the northern slopes of Caradon Hill, approached along the embankment of the railway.

The parlous remains of the boiler house adjoin the more substantial walls that needed to support heavy machinery.

The pumping engine house at Bellingham's Shaft, constructed in 1886 after the sett had been incorporated into Marke Valley Mine. The less well preserved stamps engine house and chimney stack is on the left.

The remains of an engine house at West Phoenix Mine.

Prosper (South Phoenix). It was worked for tin from relatively shallow excavations. Its last manifestation was an attempt by neighbouring Marke Valley Mines in 1883 to use the sett, again for tin. A 70 inch pumping engine and house were erected at Bellingham's Shaft in 1886, but they met with little success and the venture was abandoned four years later. An embankment, with a small arched granite conduit built through it so as not to impede a stream, once supported the railway siding to the mine, while the bridge that once crossed the road was demolished by American troops during WW2.

G. WEST PHOENIX MINE (Map 109 - 253713)

To the west of Cheesewring is the old Witheybrook Mine that once relied on a horse-engine because there was insufficient surface water to use a water wheel. In 1851 it was worked as West Phoenix, when a 30 inch steam engine was used, but the venture was not successful and closed in 1863. However, incorporation into Phoenix United in 1870 brought greater investment in the mine. Soon ten engines were at work, and a link created to the Liskeard and Caradon Railway.

THE CHARLESTOWN MINES

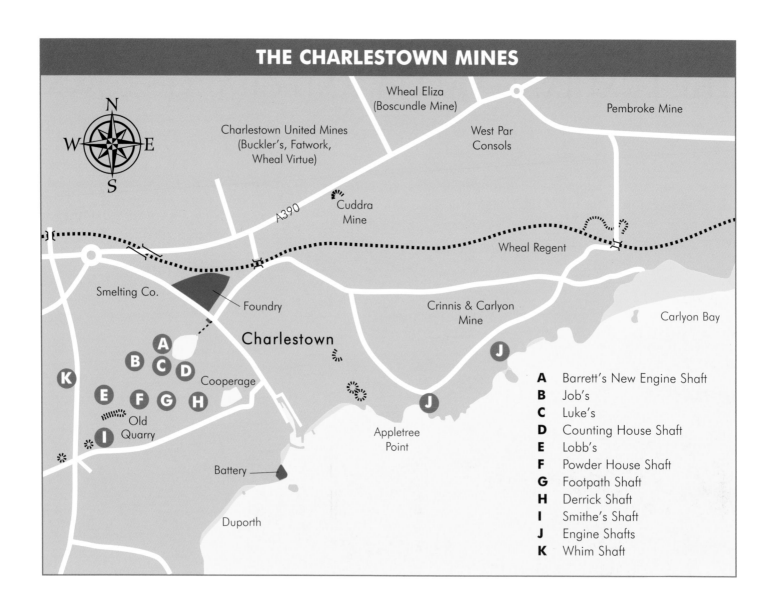

Wheal Eliza
(Boscundle Mine)

Pembroke Mine

Charlestown United Mines
(Buckler's, Fatwork,
Wheal Virtue)

West Par
Consols

A390

Cuddra
Mine

Wheal Regent

Smelting Co.

Foundry

Charlestown

Crinnis & Carlyon
Mine

Carlyon Bay

Cooperage

Old
Quarry

Appletree
Point

Battery

Duporth

A Barrett's New Engine Shaft
B Job's
C Luke's
D Counting House Shaft
E Lobb's
F Powder House Shaft
G Footpath Shaft
H Derrick Shaft
I Smithe's Shaft
J Engine Shafts
K Whim Shaft

Chapter 3

THE LUXULYAN VALLEY AND CHARLESTOWN

These two sites are largely the work of two visionary men. The first was Joseph Thomas Austen (1782-1850) who had married the heiress of the Treffry family, and whose ancestral home was Place at Fowey. In 1839 he changed his name to Treffry. The second was Charles Rashleigh.

An dramatic early nineteenth century engraving of tin mining near Luxulyan.

Luxulyan Viaduct and Aqueduct.

A. THE TREFFRY VIADUCT AND AQUEDUCT (Map 107 - 055572)

Tantalising glimpses of this magnificent granite structure can be spied through the trees as one approaches up the steep wooded valley. Seemingly remote today, it was once at the centre of an industrial octopus, just one tentacle that reached across the 201-metre void to link the harbour at Par with its north coast counterpart at Newquay. To traverse the valley originally an embankment had been considered, but this would have been more expensive than the viaduct. Designed by James Palmer, it not only carried the railway, but beneath it a chamber was incorporated to serve as an aqueduct, the water tamed by a leat to power machinery. Work began in 1839 and was completed in three years, the 5,664 cubic metres of granite being raised using blocks and pulleys, reaching nearly 30 metres above the Par River. The coat of arms of the man behind it, and who paid the £7,000 construction costs, Joseph Thomas Treffry, was carved on the northern side in the centre of the ten arches, while the shield on the southern side was left for a future inscription but still remains blank. Each arch is of 12 metres span. William Pease, Treffry's Land Steward, acted as superintendent of works. The line crossing the viaduct continued to be used until 1933.

The area was not just connected with metalliferous mining; as well as copper, granite and china clay were important commodities. Within the valley were granite quarries that supplied stone for not only the railway sleepers but such illustrious projects as London Bridge, Liverpool pier head and even the docks at Genoa. But the most celebrated example must be the 70 ton piece of Luxulyanite used to create the sarcophagus of the Duke of Wellington and now in the crypt of St Paul's Cathedral.

The railway continued via Bugle, Indian Queens and on to Newquay where the harbour had been bought by Treffry in 1838.

Water from the Luxulyan Valley was also diverted via a leat to the harbour at Charlestown.

B. CARMEARS INCLINE

The surveyor of the railway carried by the viaduct had other geographical obstacles to overcome. Having once been inundated by the sea, the route from Par was fairly level until it reached Pont's Mill. However, to climb the steep valley side an 875 metre-long

The winding house at the top of the incline.

Towards the bottom of the incline, Pont's Mill, showing the granite setts.

Far left: *The remains of the water-wheel, Luxulyan.*

Left: *One of the few remaining bolsters that secured the rails, still located on the granite sett.*

incline had to be constructed, the wagons raised by cable using a water wheel powered by the leat. Some of the spent water was channelled to the foot of the hill where it powered grinding machinery, erected by engineer William West, to crush china stone for the West of England China Clay Company (Today this runs a small hydro-electric plant.) Although generally running downhill, construction of the incline could not have been easy, for it required both a cutting through the granite hillside and an embankment, as well as a dog-leg half way down, whilst a bridge traversed it carrying a private carriage drive known as the Velvet Path. The incline was used until 1874.

The car park at Pont's Mill (Map 107 - 074562) is a short walk from the incline and the footpath following the canal.

C. PAR CANAL

At the foot of the incline the cargo was transhipped to barges that ran along a 5 km canal to the port of Par. Pulled by horses, these had a capacity of 52 tons and had to negotiate three locks. The canal also served the mines on the neighbouring hill at Fowey Consols, Lanescot (actually some distance from Fowey), from where a further inclined plane and tunnel terminated at the coal yard next to Austen's engine house. The canal was augmented by an accompanying tramway, later replaced by a railway track.

Par Canal with the railway running beside it.

Today a path follows the tramway and canal, now more like a fast-flowing stream, past St Blazey, to Par Green and within sight of the harbour.

D. FOWEY CONSOLS (Map 107 - 083559)

John Roper's map of Cornwall of 1805 clearly shows Polgooth Mine and a 'blowing house' at St Austell. However, this once important mine would soon be eclipsed. Treffry used his considerable wealth for mining ventures such as Fowey Consols, in which he held the vast majority of shares. This he began in 1822 by combining the defunct Wheal Treasure, Wheal Fortune and Wheal Chance mines,

The last remains of the railway sidings at Pont's Mill. Nearby, on the footpath to St Blazey, is a remnant of narrow-gauge track.

to which neighbouring Lanescot Mine was later incorporated. Soon it would become the largest copper mine east of Gwennap.

Near the canal at St Blazey William West (1801-1879) built the Foundry and Engine Works in 1848. This supplied much of the machinery for the local mines, as well as ones abroad. West's home was a short distance up the hillside behind the foundry at Tredenham, but the well respected and successful engineer and businessman also acquired other local estates, including Penquite and Roselyon. The foundry closed in 1891; the site is now owned by builders merchants, Travis Perkins, who have retained the square chimney stack and some of the old buildings.

West erected much of the machinery for Fowey Consols, including the celebrated 80-inch pumping engine completed in 1834 that was so well engineered that it was not only powerful but quiet-running. It was initially used to supplement the 13 water wheels which were an economical way of draining the mine. Between 1822 and 1867 some 319,790 tons of copper were produced from the 20 lodes found here. In 1838 the mine employed 1,680 people. It would be the first one in the area to be provided with a man-engine in 1851, operating to a depth of 280 fathoms (512 m) and worked by a 30 inch diameter water wheel.

Despite its success, like many others it succumbed to the copper slump of the 1860s and finally closed in 1870. Now only Austen's engine house stands like a beacon on the skyline, yet is ivy-clad and inaccessible. The record-breaking public engine trials that took place here in 1835 have been forgotten. Today, apart the old track through the sett that follows the same course as De La Beche's map of 1839, no-one would know that this extensive and important mine had existed here. Once it was one of the best equipped of any mine, boasting its own clock tower, barracks for the miners, a rope walk, as well as

An engine house built at Treesmill in 1837 as part of Fowey Consols.

the usual count house, ore floors, timber yard, stables and smithy. Even most of the spoil heaps have gone or are hidden by vegetation.

West was also responsible for rescuing Phoenix United near Liskeard, where he switched from being not just the engineer but a majority shareholder to prove his faith in the mine's ability to produce tin rather than copper. To show their gratitude 500 miners presented him with a fine clock in 1870.

E. PAR HARBOUR (Map 107 - 077527)

The harbour at the terminus of the canal was also the brainchild of Treffry, constructed between 1829 and 1840 to serve the local mines. Nearby was Par Lead Smelting Works that required a 72 metre-tall chimney stack to carry away the toxic fumes, constructed of bricks made from mud dredged from the harbour. The works closed in 1885 and Par Stack, once the tallest in Cornwall, was demolished in 1907. Nothing of the enterprise remains today.

Par Consols (Map Ref. - 073533) once occupied 'The Mount', the hill behind the harbour, and was connected to the wharves by an inclined plane. From 1840 copper was extracted here, and later tin. A prosperous enterprise for the chief adventurer, Joseph

The huge Par Stack has had a wedge of brickwork removed prior to demolition in 1907.

Citizens of Par stand atop the remains of the fallen stack on 23 August 1907.

Par harbour in the 1900s. Par Consols mine stood behind the vantage point of the photographer in the image. The smelters and chimney of Par Stack are on the far left.

Austen, in 1849 it provided a profit of £19,200 from the sale of these ores, the highest amount that year for a Cornish mine. Six years later it was the second largest tin producer in the county after Great Wheal Vor near Helston. At one time it boasted no less than 15 pumping engines and whims, as well as steam-driven stamps and a sawmill. However, by the 1860s it too was in trouble, and most of the machinery at both Fowey Consols and Par Consols were advertised for sale in 1867, although the depressed state of the industry meant there were few takers.

Rather remarkably, like many mines, nothing of it survives today. Similarly at Par Harbour, for many years now used for shipping china clay, there is no evidence of its former cargo. At the time of writing it is owned by the French clay firm Imerys, but faces an uncertain future. There is no public access.

F. CHARLESTOWN (Map 107 - 038517)

The second personality and driving force in mid-Cornwall was local landowner and entrepreneur Charles Rashleigh (1747-1823). Originally from Menabilly near Fowey, he took up residence at Duporth Manor near Charlestown. In 1791 he organised the construction of a new harbour based on plans by John Smeaton, starting with a pier, then excavating a dock basin in a natural inlet. Once a shipyard existed at the landward end, but this along with the slipway was lost when the dock was extended. China clay and ores were shipped out, while coal, limestone and timber were brought in.

The dock required a supply of water for maintaining the level and occasionally flushing out accumulated silt and debris, so a leat was constructed, running from high ground at Luxulyan, through a tunnel, to two ponds on the western side of the village that served as reservoirs. The water finally emerged at the northern end of the basin.

The settlement had grown from modest beginnings; a few fishermen's cottages and three pilchard cellars where the catch was processed. The *Content* pilchard cellar, one of the

A clay chute protrudes over Charlestown Harbour. Above it with timber-clad first floor is the former count house, later the Estate Office. This inner part of the harbour is an extension; it once contained a boatyard and slipway.

Charlestown Harbour has changed little over the years. However, an engine house near Appletree Point, above the pier, can just be discerned.

oldest buildings in the village, survives as a private residence above the cliffs and the eastern shingle beach.

Developing the fishing hamlet of West Polmear, Rashleigh was able to plan the settlement around a broad road leading from Mount Charles - remaining the widest of any village in the county. Still undulating today, it suffered from the heavy loads that passed over it in all weathers, and was only metalled in 1912. The village would be re-named in his honour.

Fearing attacks from Napoleonic France, a gun battery was built in about 1793 on the westerly prominence overlooking the harbour mouth. Crinnis Cliff Battery (or Charlestown Gun Battery) as it was known, was equipped with four 18-pounder cannon, upgraded to 24-pounders in 1860, and later 32-pounders with a two-mile range. A company of artillery volunteers was raised from the estate workers, and they maintained a regular gun-drill at the battery until 1860. Although lacking armaments, it is well preserved and only a short walk up the coastal footpath. The gun platforms and the walls of the gunpowder magazine can still be seen. (Map 107 - 039513)

Today it is hard to appreciate that this seemingly unspoilt village and former clay port was once at the heart of a very prosperous metalliferous mining industry and surrounded by mines (see Charlestown Mines map). Rich seams of copper were found at Crinnis Cliff Mine to the east in about 1810. Some 3,792 tons were raised from here, carried by mules and shipped from Charlestown between January and April 1813, followed by over 36,000 tons in the next three years. Levels even ran out under the sea.

On the western edge of the village was South Polmear Mine; now just a few dumps are discernable by the side of Duporth Road ('Brick Hill'). The old workings have been restored to agriculture and woodland with no public right of way. However, old adits can be seen in the cliffs by the beach.

Charlestown United Mines, for a time run by John Taylor who was also in charge of nearby Pembroke Mine, were located to the north of the present A390 at Holmbush (not

Holes in the wall of the former 'Content' pilchard cellar through which rods would be placed that compressed the pilchards.

The Battery, Charlestown, guards the entrance to the once busy harbour.

One of the lime kilns at Charlestown. The gun store for the battery abuts it on the left.

The old count house, Charlestown.

to be mistaken with the Holmbush Mining Company of Callington). These works have vanished beneath buildings, but in the first half of the nineteenth century were particularly prosperous mines, rich in both tin and copper: 431 men, 120 women and 263 children were employed here in 1838. Steam as well as water-driven stamps were employed using a series of water wheels, with whim shafts dug to raise ore besides the typical engine shafts.

The 1851 census reveals that of the 283 adults residing in the village there were ten miners, one of whom also worked as a cooper, plus one mine agent. (There were also ten other coopers.) Other notable occupations included a tea dealer and hobbler.

To handle the ore being sent to the smelters in Swansea the village was provided with several ore floors. An example is now the car park of the Rashleigh Arms, the cobbles forming the surface being created from ballast from in-bound ships. Other ore floors included the site of the present recreation ground. Behind this and nestling in the valley a long ropewalk was established by the time a map of Charlestown Estate was drawn in 1825. Today's main public car park was a coal yard, with an adjoining timber yard. There was also a limestone floor, and seven lime kilns, one of which stood on the site of the Harbourmaster's Round House overlooking the outer harbour. The lime was used by farmers to counteract the acidic soil. The village also had a count house opposite the inn's car park, a smithy and a granary. Three cooperages provided casks for pilchards, china clay as well as more obvious liquids.

As the village grew and prospered other amenities were added: a Methodist Chapel in 1827; St Paul's Church, consecrated in 1851; and a village school in 1895.

As the mines struggled, china clay began to supplant ore. The Shipwreck and Heritage Centre, providing an insight into the village's life and our maritime legacy, is housed in part of a former clay dry. A short tunnel that runs beneath Quay Road enabled the dried clay to be taken by trams via an enclosed gantry to a series of chutes, from where is was directed into the holds of ships, a process which left a bright coating of fine white dust on the surroundings. The position of the gantry can still be discerned running along the top of the harbour wall. The inner basin could eventually take vessels of up to 600 tons, but it was always a spectacle to see them negotiate the protruding 'banjo' of the outer harbour at high tide, limiting factors that led to trade drying up during the 1990s, at a time when the port became home to the 'Square Sail' fleet.

Charlestown Leat that fed into the harbour also provided water power as it entered the village by the side of the road. On the western side was a mill and Charlestown Tin Smelting Company (Map Ref. - 032522) that took advantage of the water supply as well as the locally won ore until 1885, and on the opposite side Charlestown Foundry that once had four water wheels, one of which can still be seen. The leat ran through the neighbouring fields and also supplied the ponds. This system pre-dated the foundry which was developed on High Leat Field and Low Leat Field, as they were known at the time of an 1825 map of the Estate.

A redundant china clay chute on the quay at Charlestown.

G. CHARLESTOWN FOUNDRY AND IRONWORKS (Map 107 - 035523)

Charlestown Foundry was started in 1827 by J and R Mitchell, two brothers from Redruth, to serve the local mines. The business was taken over eight years later by a Redruth boiler-maker, James Thomas and his two sons, James and Edwin. He obviously had a view to expanding the business, adding '& Ironworks Ltd.' to the appellation. James Junior produced the drawings, including some of the first blueprints to be used in Cornwall, while his brother acted as manager. The company was responsible for supplying equipment for St Austell's new gas works in 1836, as well as furnishing the local mines. Their products ranged from Cornish shovels to kibbles made from scrap wrought iron, as well as boilers and components for steam engines. After the firm was acquired by Thomas Martyn in 1885 a further adjunct became bridge-making, some being supplied to India. Prefabricated components for a beam engine to be set up in Mexico were also produced, a requirement being that the parts had to be light enough to be carried over the mountains by mule.

As metalliferous mining contracted, the company found more work in the china clay industry, and Carbean Clay Dry was constructed on the northern part of the site in 1906 - 7. Now clay slurry was piped here from the clay works rather than having to be carried in bulk through the streets in horse-drawn wagons. In 1935 the foundry, then known as Charlestown Engineering, became part of English China Clays.

During the war years the company produced munitions, gun mountings and parts for tanks and armoured cars, as well as contributing components for the Mulberry Harbours used during the D-Day landings in Normandy. Then the main buildings were disguised with camouflage paint.

After the war the foundry resumed work for the clay industry, typically producing monitors, filter presses and gravel pumps. New departments also catered for the repair and maintenance of machinery, as well as galvanising and fabrication. However, retraction in the clay industry led to Charlestown Engineering being sold off in 1991. After a further change of ownership in 1994 the foundry finally closed in 2003, then the site was redeveloped.

A few features have been preserved; the façade of the machine shop facing the road - all that remained of the original building, replaced by a larger one during the Second World War - has been incorporated into new buildings, the higher boundary wall next to Charlestown Road, which includes evidence of an old chute that opened on to the highway, and a gateway. The nineteenth-century Pattern Store, although modified and extended over the years, has been retained, along with the 30 foot diameter water wheel built at the foundry in 1852 to operate tilt hammers. An overshot wheel, it was fed by a siphon pipe that stands alongside.

A decorative cast-iron signpost at St Ewe, cast at Charlestown Foundry.

GWENNAP

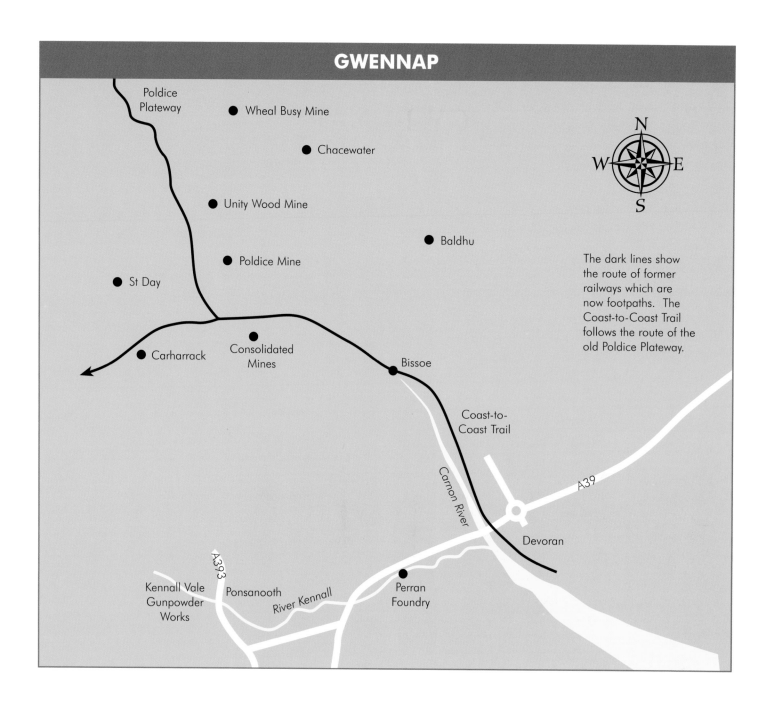

The dark lines show the route of former railways which are now footpaths. The Coast-to-Coast Trail follows the route of the old Poldice Plateway.

Chapter 4
GWENNAP

The Gwennap area is found to the east of Redruth, around the once prosperous mining community of St Day. As well as numerous mines linked by tramways, the area included Perran Foundry, Devoran quays and Kennall Vale Gunpowder Works. Each of these operations made its own unique contribution to the local mining industry.

A. THE MINES

There were active mines here at least as early as the Tudor period, but they were hampered by the limitations of drainage and smelting. Although small local smelters were established, much of the ore was sent to South Wales or Bristol.

St Day Church fell into disrepair as mining fortunes declined. At one time the prosperous village had seven places of worship, as well as nine public houses.

The area around St Day was once the richest copper producing region in the world. The photograph (left) shows the workings at Bissa Pool c.1900, at the end of the mining boom.

When copper was first discovered at Wheal Virgin in 1757, £15,000 worth of ore was won in just five weeks from close to the surface. This obviously encouraged other adventurers to the area, so that by 1770 there were some ninety mines.

However, the end of the eighteenth century saw a recession; profits fell as Cornish copper mines fought fresh competition from mines at Parys Mountain, Anglesey, where large deposits were close to the surface and easily won without the need for pumps. Allied with over-production in the local mines, continued engine dues and low tin prices, many mines in the Gwennap area were forced to stop work. Thousands of miners found themselves unemployed, and led to a series of food riots. The problems were exacerbated by the unfair truck system, whereby often miners were paid in tokens that could only be redeemed at the mines' own outlets, frequently at inflated prices.

B. DRAINAGE AND THE GREAT COUNTY ADIT

One of the major concerns was keeping the mines free from water. Where possible adits were driven into the sides of valleys or cliffs, or water wheels employed. However, when the geography was unfavourable other methods had to be used. In the 1720s steam engines were being installed in some of the more prosperous mines, the atmospheric engine having been invented by Dartmouth blacksmith Thomas Newcomen. Inefficient, and demanding large amounts of coal, these 'fire' engines did enable the mines to be kept free of water to a depth of about 60 fathoms.

Engineers such as Richard Trevithick (1771-1833), John Smeaton (1724-92) and the Hornblowers, who installed most of the Newcomen engines, strove to improve the design. However, it was James Watt's refinement using a separate condenser that drastically reduced the coal consumption while increasing the engine's power using the pressure of steam as opposed to atmospheric pressure. The first Watt engine in Cornwall was installed at Chacewater Mine (Wheal Busy) in 1777, pumping to a depth of 45 fathoms.

Yet there was a catch. Under the patent obtained with Watt's partner, Matthew Boulton, the mines had to pay an annual sum of approximately a third of the saving they had made over the earlier engine. This 'duty' had to be paid for 25 years or alternatively a one-off payment equivalent to ten years' dues. This led to increasing friction between Boulton and Watt and the mine adventurers, but even appeals to Parliament failed to

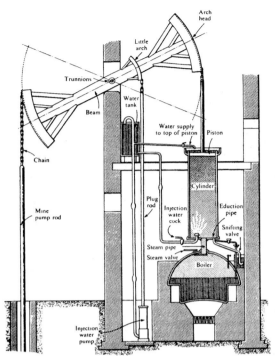

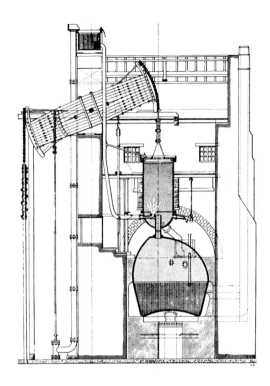

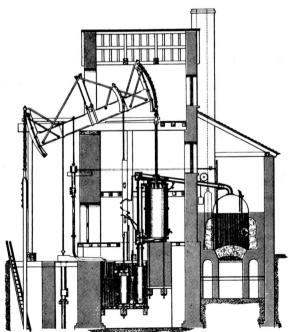

Top left: *The layout of a typical Newcomen atmospheric engine c.1715.*

Top right: *Layout of John Smeaton's atmospheric engine as installed at Chacewater Mine, erected in 1775.*

Left: *Layout of a typical Boulton and Watt atmospheric engine c.1780 which employed a separate condenser thus greatly improving efficiency.*

63

The remains of a Brunton calciner at Great Wheal Busy, from when the mine turned to arsenic production in about 1910. It originally had a pyramidal roof. To the left once stood a large mill building.

The cast iron lintels of the old smithy were made at Perran Foundry in 1872.

change the situation. Furthermore, the extensive patents held by Boulton and Watt impeded developments by other engineers such as Trevithick, Jonathan Hornblower and Edward Bull, who took to ignoring their injunctions.

Even when the water was put to good use there could be problems. At Great Wheal Busy, (Map 104 - 739447) formerly Chacewater Mine, the water raised was found to be particularly corrosive and even contaminated the surface water, necessitating the frequent replacement of boilers. Eventually a supply of clean water was sourced from a neighbouring mine. A wide range of successive pumping engines were installed here during the life of the mine.

No wonder The Great County Adit, first started in 1748 by Sir William Lemon, chief adventurer of Poldice Mine, and his manager, John Williams, continued to be extended, for it formed a cheap and effective method of draining not just their own mine but a number of others while offering the possibility of fresh strikes during construction. Like a tree, branches were extended in a radius from Pennance Mine near Lanner in the west

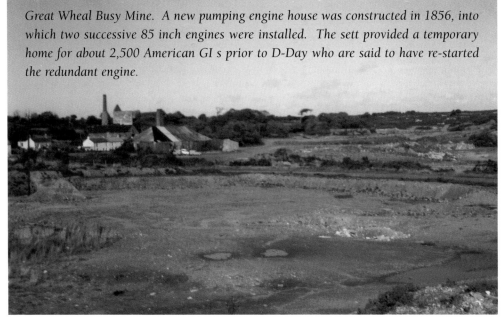

Great Wheal Busy Mine. A new pumping engine house was constructed in 1856, into which two successive 85 inch engines were installed. The sett provided a temporary home for about 2,500 American GI s prior to D-Day who are said to have re-started the redundant engine.

to Killifreth Mine near Chacewater in the east, in a complex of some 64 km of tunnels. These drained into the upper course of the Carnon River close to Twelveheads (Map 105 - 761421) near Bissoe, and so into the Fal at Devoran. By 1778 the system had been extended through Wheal Busy to North Downs and Wheal Peevor, incorporating the parishes of Gwennap, Chacewater, St Day and Scorrier. By the 1860s over 30 beam engines were employed, estimated to have eventually discharged some 13 million gallons per day from over 60 mines. Such was the peak volume that the adit had to be duplicated in places. It was a splendid example of co-operation between mines, and saved a large amount of money in pumping costs, but there was still a price to pay; heavy rains during the winter of 1876 led to large amounts of silt from the adit being deposited at Devoran, permanently hindering navigation.

Boulton and Watt once had financial interests in Consolidated Mines. Near the surviving clock tower at Wheal Maid, now surrounded by additional waste material from Mount Wellington and Wheal Jane that was dumped there during the 1970s and '80s, the first steam whim in Cornwall was erected by them in 1784.

The impressive clock tower at Consolidated Mines survives in the midst of many hectares of spoil, and hints at the mineral wealth of this area.

John Taylor had taken over its affairs in 1819, turning it from a redundant operation to one employing over 3,000 people and producing a record 23,194 tons of copper twenty years later. He installed some of the most powerful engines in Cornwall. The old copper mine of United Downs incorporated the wonderfully named Ale and Cakes and Wheal Cupboard (formerly Metal Works), as well as Consolidated Mines in 1857 and Wheal Clifford in 1861, after which they were collectively known as Clifford Amalgamated. At its peak this enterprise was running a record 18 steam engines, including Taylor's celebrated 85 inch pumping engine. However, after the mid-1850s production slumped. Operations ceased in 1870 due to the depression in the copper market, putting 1,300 miners out of work. Despite its size and importance little evidence of it remains today apart from many hectares of spoil.

It was to serve Consolidated Mines that in 1824 Taylor constructed the Redruth and Chasewater Railway. This ran from Pednandrea in Redruth via Carharrick, then followed the Carnon Valley down through Bissoe to Devoran and Point, where wharves were built to cater for it. A branch line ran west to Buller Downs and the main Gwennap mines. It was originally a horse-drawn tram road with an uncommon 4 foot gauge, but was converted for locomotives in 1854 when two tank engines, *Miner* and *Smelter*, were acquired. The line closed in 1915.

C. THE MINERAL TRAMWAYS HERITAGE PROJECT

This created approximately 29 km of interlinked trails on the routes of former tramways. These are designed to improve access to our mining heritage along mainly traffic-free routes.

The Redruth and Chasewater Railway Trail follows much of the original route and runs from Twelveheads (Map 105 - 761424) past the sett of Consolidated Mines, the villages of Carharrack and Lanner to Redruth. Here it connects with the Great Flat Lode Trail, a circular 12 km route which includes part of the former Basset Mine tramway which used to take ore for processing at the nearby stamps.

Smelter was the first two locomotives to be put into service on the Redruth & Chacewater railway on 1 December 1854. The other locomotive was named *Miner*.

The 17.5 km Coast to Coast Trail from Portreath to Devoran, and the Portreath Branchline Trail, also link up with other pathways in theCamborne/ Redruth area. The Portreath Incline linked the village with the Portreath to Poldice Tramroad. When constructed in 1809 it was the first surface-level tramway in Cornwall, providing a much

An impressive engine house at Unity Wood Mine next to Poldice. Nearby ran the Portreath to Poldice Tramway, and granite sleepers can still be seen in the footpath beside the lane.

The route of The Coast to Coast Trail is well marked.

more reliable transport network than the unmade mule tracks it replaced. It was originally laid as a 3 foot gauge plateway, using horse-drawn wagons.

D. PORTREATH (Map 104 - 655453)

The two rectangular granite basins were constructed in 1800 and 1846 to facilitate shipments of ore to Swansea. A long breakwater close to the cliffs was also built to provide deep water at the harbour's mouth. At its peak around 1840 some 100,000 tons of copper a year were being exported from here, while coal was brought in on the return journey. Large coal and ore floors occupied the flat ground to the west of the harbour, now largely built over. However, the steep ginger-coloured granite incline incorporating an arched bridge that linked the port with the tramway survives on the western slopes of the valley. A stationary engine was used to haul up the wagons.

E. DEVORAN (Map 105 - 795390)

Devoran was a planned new town, and not just created as a mineral port, but for general commerce. Its growth saw the decline of the port of Penryn. Once a hive of activity, today this sleepy village lying low beside the heavily silted river, is a very different place. The wharves were once full of ore awaiting shipment to the smelters, with numerous ships tied up alongside unloading coal and timber. The nearby Norway Inn (778388) derives its name from the source of the shaft timbering, pit props, headframes, pump rods, building materials and so forth. The line continued along the river bank to Point (809385) where there were further wharves providing far better access and facilities than those that had once been reached by pack-horse at Pill Quay (826387) or Roundway Quay (838404) in isolated wooded inlets further up the Fal estuary.

Today the car park makes a good starting point for a trip along the Coast to Coast Trail.

A cast-iron lintel at Perran Foundry, bearing the date 1791.

F. PERRAN FOUNDRY, PERRANARWORTHAL (Map 105 - 775385)

This facility was established in 1791 at Perran Wharf, a convenient tidal quay at which to land supplies of coal and iron ore and where there were fresh water supplies from Kennall Vale. The main instigators were the Foxes of Falmouth, important shipping merchants with interests in the Gwennap mines, along with other Quaker partners. George Croker Fox, succeeded by his sons George and Robert, developed the business.

At its peak the foundry employed 400 people. In 1792 they leased the Neath Abbey Iron Works, including coal and iron mines, in South Wales, and their own ships were used to bring in raw materials. (This arrangement would end when the concern was acquired by Benjamin Sampson.) Pig-iron was also brought in from Coalbrookdale.

Caroline Fox described the casting of a bob from 14 tons of iron in 1840 as '*a magnificent spectacle, and induced sundry allusions to Vulcan's forge and other classical subjects.*' She also noted, '*This beam was the largest they had ever cast, and its fame had attracted almost the whole population of Perran, who looked highly picturesque by the light of the liquid iron.*'

An ornate cast-iron footbridge still crosses the stream.

Perran Foundry reached its apogee in the 1840s and 50s when it was probably building as many engines as Harvey & Co. or Copperhouse at Hayle. It maintained a friendly rivalry with Harvey's, yet sometimes sharing contracts. Engines and equipment produced here were exported worldwide, often in component-form so they could be transported by mule to remote locations in such places as Mexico, Australia or South America.

In the 1860s, as well as pattern shops, a moulding shop and hammer mill, the foundry even had its own gas works, pig iron quay and a travelling crane. A leat supplied water to five cast-iron water wheels and these were augmented by two steam engines.

The sad remains of foundry buildings. Another cast-iron lintel can just be discerned above the walled-up doorway on the right.

The foundry closed in 1879. Today the 2.5 hectare site is Grade 2 listed, but has been in a dilapidated state for many years and awaits re-development at the time of writing. The evocative cast-iron arches with the name over the entrance survives.

G. KENNALL VALE GUNPOWDER WORKS near Ponsanooth (Map 104 - 753376)

Today the constant sound of running water is a reminder of one reason for the choice of location for this establishment in about 1812 within a heavily wooded valley. A leat system was used to provide water to a number of parts of the site, including an incorporating mill, with the wheel pit between two mill buildings. The remains of the overshot wheel rim can be seen, along with two large gear wheels within the walls that drove vertical millstones. A millstone now stands in front of the entrance of Kennall Vale School.

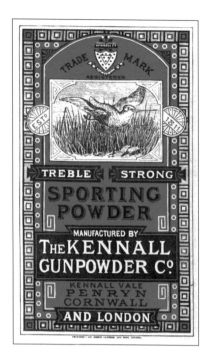

A label for the product of the gunpowder works.

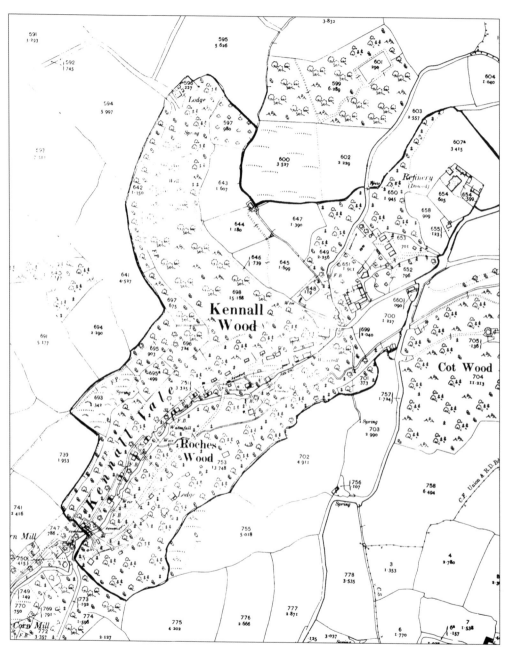

The Kennall Vale gunpowder works occupied much of the valley as this map shows. The plentiful supply of water and its relative remoteness made this an ideal site for the production of gunpowder.

Some 50 people were employed here in the 1860s, but with the advent of high explosives during the 1880s demand dropped and the factory closed in about 1910. One mill was then used to drive a compressor to power air tools used in the small granite quarry set into the hillside on the far side of the river. This had provided materials for most of the buildings and the substantial revetments. There were sulphur mills and magazines, plus various other dispersed structures that can still be seen, though it is hard to construe their purposes today.

Now set in a nature reserve, the trees were actually planted by the Kennall Gunpowder Company to help retain a damp atmosphere, as well as provide protection should there be an explosion. Such an accident did occur in 1838, resulting in much damage, the death of one man and the serious injury of another.

A collection of surviving buildings at Kennall Vale Gunpowder Works stand in the shadows of dense woodland.

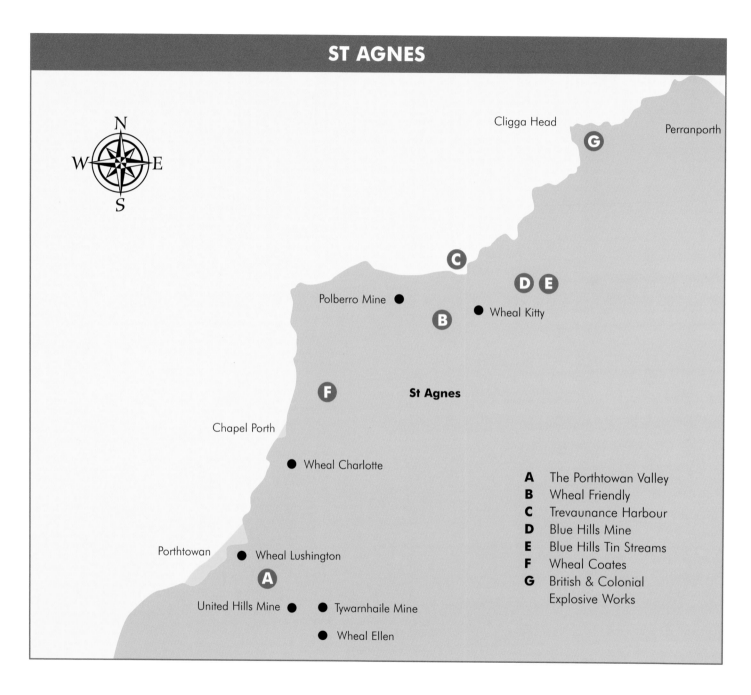

Cligga Head

Perranporth

G

C

Polberro Mine ●

B

D **E**

● Wheal Kitty

St Agnes

F

Chapel Porth

● Wheal Charlotte

Porthtowan

● Wheal Lushington

A

United Hills Mine ● ● Tywarnhaile Mine

● Wheal Ellen

A The Porthtowan Valley
B Wheal Friendly
C Trevaunance Harbour
D Blue Hills Mine
E Blue Hills Tin Streams
F Wheal Coates
G British & Colonial
Explosive Works

Chapter 5
ST AGNES

The area stretches along the north Cornish coast from Porthtowan to Perranporth, and includes a cluster of mines around the village of St Agnes itself. It contained some of the last working mines, many continuing well into the twentieth century.

A. THE PORTHTOWAN VALLEY

Within the valley leading down to the sea can be found Wheal Ellen (Map 104 - 703469), Tywarnhaile Mines (700472) and United Hills (696475). The latter was once run by

Porthtowan, showing Wheal Lushington near the beach. This engine house was built in the 1880s, but the company went bankrupt before the engine could be installed. It was subsequently converted to a dwelling house and is now inconspicuous amongst modern buildings.

Wheal Ellen, with its distinctive castellated chimney stack.

Wheal Friendly, with Wheal Kitty across the valley in the background.

John Taylor, records showing it produced over 4,000 tons of copper in 1838, when 359 people were employed there. Along with Wheal Rock, it would be incorporated into Tywarnhaile Mines. This enterprise had produced over 6,000 tons of copper in 1850. At about this time it had an unusual hauling machine located underground but driven by a pumping engine on the surface, via its pump rod. In 1906 it would also be the first mine in Cornwall to use electric pumps.

B. WHEAL FRIENDLY (Map 104 - 720512)

Now on the edge of a residential area and approached via a footpath from Trevaunance Road, Wheal Friendly overlooks the coast and Trevaunance Cove. Despite being Grade 2 listed, the surviving engine house was saved from developers in 2007 when locals objected to plans to convert it into a holiday complex. A later survivor, the mine acquired the 60 inch engine from neighbouring Polberro (715514) in about 1900. This mine itself, which had been Christened Royal Polberro Consols following a visit by Queen Victoria in 1846, re-opened between 1937 and 1941, and the engine house of Turnavore Shaft where Wheal Friendly's pumping engine originally worked, can be seen across the valley.

Wheal Friendly's stamps were located on unstable killas (sedimentary rock), and due to the reverberations became dislodged and had to be abandoned. Ore was then processed at the Jericho stamps of West Wheal Kitty with which it was already associated. Due to lack of space, being so close to St Agnes, the Jericho Stamps were remote from the mine and located at the higher end of Trevellas Coombe, with the ore being transported there in wagons. After West Wheal Kitty closed in 1916, Wheal Friendly soldiered on for a couple more years. One ruined engine house of West Wheal Kitty survives amongst the houses of St Agnes (718508).

Wheal Kitty itself was on the eastern side of the village. (724513). Adventurers re-opened this mine in 1926 using the 65 inch engine built by Perran Foundry in 1852. It would be the last mine to work in the district, closing in just four years, after which the venerable old engine was scrapped. The pumping engine house at Sara's Shaft, constructed in 1910, has been converted to office use and provides an indication of the grandeur these buildings once possessed. The old boiler and compressor house has also been refurbished and is now commercial premises. Nearby are the remains of the mill, stamps and dressing floors, whilst amongst the heather, burrows provide evidence of the once extensive mining activity in the area.

Sara's Shaft engine house at Wheal Kitty, beautifully restored and used as commercial premises.

Gooninnis Mine, standing on the hill above St Agnes, displays well built brick arched window openings and a crenellated chimney top. This decorative feature was found on other engine houses in the area, such as at Wheal Friendly, Wheal Golden at Perranporth, and Wheal Ellen, near Porthtowan, suggesting a common contractor.

A pile of granite blocks is all that remains of the breakwater at Trevaunance Cove.

C. TREVAUNANCE HARBOUR (721517)

No less than five attempts were made by the Tonkin family, the lords of the manor, to construct an artificial harbour to serve the mines of the area. However, on this exposed spot they were at the mercy of the Atlantic storms. The small breakwater pier was destroyed in 1915. The harbour's viability was restricted by its construction using overhanging wooden staging, requiring a horse whim to raise cargo from vessels, while ore was lowered down a chute. Despite its shortcomings as a port, between 1873 and 1877 four merchant schooners were constructed here. Near the harbour was the open cast tin mine of Wheal Luna. Looking inland from the beach one can see extensive slopes of grey scree on the cliff tops and valley sides, the whole area having been heavily worked over the years.

Taken in the mid 1890s, this photograph shows how the landscape around Trevaunance Cove had been scarred by mining in the preceding decades. Attempts to construct a permanent port here proved impossible.

D. BLUE HILLS MINE (728517)

The neighbouring valley of Trevellas Coombe was also heavily mined, and various remains of Blue Hills Mine, which closed in 1897, can be seen today including the crumbling engine house where a 70 inch pumping engine operated. The steep mine track forms a daunting section of the Land's End Trial, traditionally run each Easter by The Motor Cycling Club.

E. BLUE HILL TIN STREAMS

The valley floor once contained extensive tin stream works, used to recover any tin that could be gleaned from the river. Reviving the ancient practice, Blue Hills Tin Streams was opened in 2001. This attraction provides an insight into how the tin was once

Blue Hills Tin Streams, a recent incarnation of an ancient process.

The settling lagoon at Blue Hills Tin Steams.

Much-photographed Towanroath pumping engine house, Wheal Coates.

Right: *The whim engine house at Wheal Coates. The buff-coloured brickwork is deliberately contrasting restoration.*

Far right: *The 1872-3 stamps and whim engine house above the dressing floors, with the stack of the calciner on the left.*

Above: *Atmospheric Wheal Coates – the higher workings.*

Right: *The crumbling remains of Wheal Charlotte stand on the cliff top surrounded by 'deads'. Wheal Coates can been seen in the background across the valley of Chapel Porth.*

processed. A small waterwheel drives a set of restored stamps and a working buddle, while a settling lagoon is also used to glean tin. Inside the new buildings are a ball mill and shaking table, further refining the ore. The resulting tin is turned into jewellery and other trinkets.

F. WHEAL COATES (700501)

Standing in defiant isolation on the gorse and heather-covered cliff tops east of Chapel Porth and in the shadow of St Agnes Beacon is Wheal Coates. Nearest to the sea is the magnificent, photogenic pumping house by the 180 metre-deep Towanroath Shaft, which appears on the back of the Cornwall County Council library card and the cover of the Ordnance Survey Explorer Map 104 of Redruth and St Agnes. Dating from 1872, the building is now in the hands of the National Trust. Further up the slope other interesting remains include the dried up pond that provided water for the dual-purpose stamps and winding engine, remains of a calciner and flue built between 1910 and 1913, as well as trial excavations.

G. BRITISH & COLONIAL EXPLOSIVE WORKS, Cligga Head (738537)

Set up to supply the nearby mines on a sloping site of 44.5 ha, the factory was established far too late in the story: active between 1893 and 1905, it was then brought back into service during the First World War. Ironically, much of the works was destroyed during the creation of RAF Perranporth (Trevellas) during the Second World War, while at the same time the old surface workings of nearby Perran St George Mine and Wheal Prudence were removed. Meanwhile Cligga Head was mined for valuable tin and wolfram during the conflict, and most of the robust reinforced concrete machine beds that survive amongst the extensive jumble of mine workings date from that period.

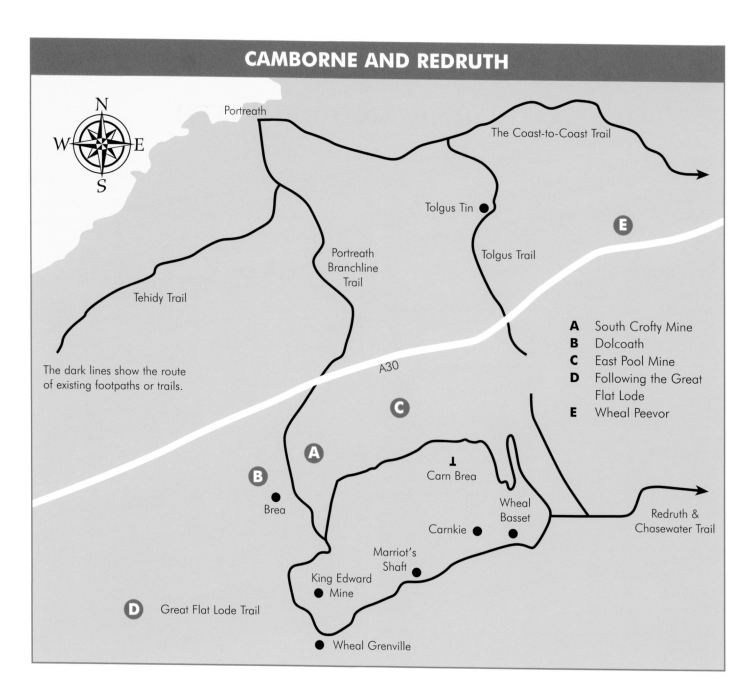

CAMBORNE AND REDRUTH

Portreath

The Coast-to-Coast Trail

Tolgus Tin ●

Tolgus Trail

Portreath
Branchline
Trail

Tehidy Trail

A30

The dark lines show the route
of existing footpaths or trails.

E

A South Crofty Mine
B Dolcoath
C East Pool Mine
D Following the Great
 Flat Lode
E Wheal Peevor

C

A

⊥
Carn Brea

B

Brea ●

Wheal
Basset

Carnkie ● ●

Marriot's
Shaft
 ●

Redruth &
Chasewater Trail

King Edward
 ● Mine

D Great Flat Lode Trail

● Wheal Grenville

Chapter 6
CAMBORNE AND REDRUTH

This was the home of not just some of the most productive mines, but also important service industries, including Bickford's Tuckingmill factory, Holman's and Camborne School of Mines.

A. SOUTH CROFTY MINE (Map 104 - 664410)

South Crofty currently offers underground tours run alongside their operations which aim to resume production of tin in 2009. The guided tours provide an interesting comparison of new and old workings and working practises.

After a short walk, dressed in Wellington boots, a white hard hat equipped with a light, and with a bright blue battery pack strapped around the midriff, parties are led

The monumental headframe and elevator, South Crofty.

Only latterly did steel replace traditional timber for these structures.

Mineral-rich rock in the roof of the tunnel, South Crofty.

through the gated entrance of the recently created Tuckingmill Decline unobtrusively set into the hillside. Entering the arched reinforced void one is confronted with a tunnel wide and tall enough to take diesel-powered scoop trams that are used to remove the rock, and frequent alcoves or 'Refuges' built into the side allow miners to retreat from their paths. These are equipped with first aid boxes and telephones. There is also a water supply and large fans feed air from the surface via large canvas tubes running along the walls. It is very wet underfoot, but the temperature is equable; rising by one degree for every hundred feet descended the tour does not go deep enough to notice much change.

At the foot of the decline are the present workings which aim to intercept fresh lodes further into the mine. There is estimated to be enough tin reserves still in the mine to last at least eighty years, as well as other valuable minerals. The old workings are still flooded below this level.

South Crofty Mine c.1910

A mine tour gives a flavour of the many hazards underground, even when wearing modern helmets and lights.

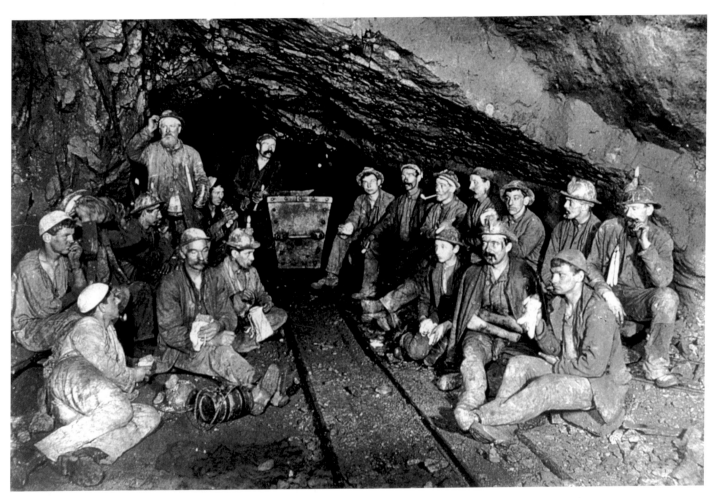

Miners at croust time in Cook's Kitchen Mine, 1893.

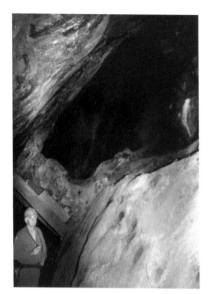

A stope on the Tincroft Lode, South Crofty, disappears into the darkness.

In places one is forced to splash through pools of water with the hue of a strong cup of tea that traverse the floor. On the roof of the tunnel, from where sporadic drips of water fall, are occasional blooms of colour - tell-tail signs of ore - while numbered labels provide a precise reference point to one's location.

When the mine closed in 1998 the lower workings quickly flooded. The 80-inch engine at Robinson's Shaft, South Crofty, was the last Cornish engine to work at a Cornish mine, being replaced by electric pumps in 1955 (see Chapter 10). Just before the workings end at a 300 metre-deep pool marking the point to which the old shafts are flooded, is an incongruous picnic table, aptly dubbed 'The Hardrock Café', where today's miners have their 'crib' or 'croust'. It is still a noisy occupation with fans roaring and drills operating, and remains, inevitably, a dirty, dusty and uncomfortable working environment.

A short flight of steps leads up to an older narrow passage that opens out into a stope, a large hand-excavated cavern angled upwards that ends somewhere in the darkness.

Winding drums, awaiting re-awakening at South Crofty.

Occasional pillars of rock have been left to support the roof, aided by stout timber props. The roving head lamps pick out occasional blooms of copper, of a bright turquoise colour that floresce in the light, or white stains of arsenical deposits. In places the small tunnels of earlier mining are revealed, some dating back to the 1600s, making this one of the oldest mines in Cornwall. They are so small it would have been difficult to turn, providing scant room to work in, let alone see what to strike by candlelight, while the malodorous tallow candles made from sheep's fat robbed men of vital oxygen.

As the levels wind on, the route follows a narrow gauge railway track where wagons were used to remove the rock. Some offshoots have been blocked by rock falls, while elsewhere the roof has been strengthened by large bolts set into the rock in fast-drying resin to hold the layers together. With miles of tunnels, few reference points, and limited visibility, it would be so easy to get lost if it wasn't for the enthusiastic and knowledgeable guide, a working miner himself.

In one stope, where the sides are angled unnervingly away from the floor, we are asked to turn off our lamps. The darkness is absolute. Total all-enveloping blackness. The guide lights a candle, the soft glow revealing something of our surroundings, but providing scant light for accurately striking the glint from the end of a tool. Yet in the early twentieth century miners eschewed the new carbide lamps, and even the early electric lamps, for the batteries were heavy and tended to leak acid, so many preferred to persevere with candles.

A modern lift conveys parties the 45 metres back to the surface. This is a relatively shallow depth, but still conveys the terrible conditions the old Cornish miners had to endure, as well as what it is like for the 16 miners who presently operate below ground. Even after less than two hours down there it is still refreshing to burst out from the modest grey lift building into the bright sunlight and breathe fresh air.

The size of the equipment can be appreciated in this view.

B. DOLCOATH (Map 104 - 660404)

Across the Tuckingmill valley can be found various remains of the once great Dolcoath mine, including New East Shaft winding engine house and New Sump Shaft compressor house. Built in 1886, the latter housed a 12 inch air compressor built by Holman Brothers that was capable of supplying air 0.8 km below ground. During the early years

The gig at the 1,900 foot level, Dolcoath Mine, circa 1890.

One of the superb photographs taken by J.C. Burrow showing the man engine at Dolcoath Mine. It was via this contraption that miners were taken to and from the deep workings each day.

Tincroft Mine, North Part

Carn Brea Mine, North Part

Tincroft Pumping Engine

Carn Brea Mine, South Part

Carn Brea Monument

Carn Brea Castle

Cook's Kitchen Mine

Cook's Kitchen Mine Office

Dolcoath Eastern Shaft

Dolcoath Stamps Erected 1892

Dolcoath Stamping Engine

This view, taken c.1893, reveals the nightmarish industrial wasteland that mining brought to Cornwall's landscape. Taken looking along the northern slopes of Carn Brea, in the region between Camborne and Redruth the view includes Dolcoath mine, the Dolcoath Valley Smithy, where Richard Trevithick is said to have performed much of his work, Cook's Kitchen Mine, Tincroft Mine, Carn Brea Mine and East Pool Mine.

of the nineteenth century 1,600 people were employed at the mine, and an average of 8,000 tons of copper ore a year was produced. In 1836 Dolcoath turned from mining copper to tin. By the time it closed in 1921 some shafts reached a depth of over 1,000 metres, making it the deepest metal mine in Britain.

C. EAST POOL MINE

Two Cornish beam engines survive here. Beside the road at Pool, at Michell's Shaft, is the engine house preserved by the National Trust containing a 30 inch whim engine built in 1887 by Holman Brothers (Map 104 - 673415). It would be the last Cornish beam whim to be installed. The mine was worked for copper and later tin, as well as some arsenic and wolfram. Nearby, Taylor's Shaft (674419) gained a 90 inch pumping engine in 1924 that had been built for Carn Brea Mines in 1892 by Harvey and Co. and costing £675. This operated a 10 metre-long cast iron bob weighing 52 tons. The chimney stack has EPAL picked out in white brick, representing East Pool & Agar Ltd., following their

Another photograph by J.C. Burrow showing the tram road in East Pool Mine.

merger in 1896, as well as being the brand-name for their arsenic. Even though the mine closed in 1945, the engine continued to operate for the benefit of South Crofty until 1954, raising water some 519 metres and helping to ensure its survival.

D. FOLLOWING THE GREAT FLAT LODE

The Great Flat Lode was discovered late in the story of South West mining, for this rich lode of tin was found in the 1870s beneath previously exploited copper deposits to the south of Carn Brea. The lode ran at an angle of 30 degrees from the horizontal, rather than the more common 70 degrees, hence its name.

One of the most productive mines in the area was Wheal Basset. Production of copper peaked in 1855-56 when the mine produced 7,856 tons, worth £66,999. However, this was a third of that produced by Devon Great Consols during the same period.

Today the dressing floors can still be seen at Carnkie (693399) where stamps broke down the ore to a fine powder, buddles separated the ore from the waste, while caliners were used to roast the tin concentrate in order to remove heavy minerals and other impurities ready for smelting at the nearby Seleggan Smelting Works.

Impressive, cathedral-like remains can also be seen at Marriot's Shaft, the South Wheal Frances section of Wheal Basset (681394) Almost 68,000 tons of copper ore and 7,000 tons of tin had been raised here by 1891. A new compound engine was installed at Marriot's Shaft in 1897-9 to help keep the mine dry, replacing an earlier engine destroyed in one of a series of fires. This vertical engine design using 40 inch high pressure and 80 inch low pressure cylinders was unique in Cornwall. It was going to be augmented by a second engine, but only the neighbouring large house was built. The engine was scrapped when the mine closed in 1918. Nearby in 1908 the large miners' dry or changing room was added.

Now a roost for birds, the stack was once much taller than this.

Impressive remains at Marriot's Shaft, Wheal Basset, once the terminus of a tramway.

Left: *Wheal Grenville. The mine closed in 1920. The bob was removed and taken to New Cook's Kitchen Shaft at South Crofty in 1922. As can be seen, the bearing mountings for the bob remain in place. The chimney stack was a victim of a lightning strike in 1897.*

Far left: *Wheal Grenville. Fortescue's Shaft pumping engine house, constructed as late as 1892. It housed a 90 inch beam engine. Behind it is the smaller winding house of the same date that housed a 28 inch rotative beam engine used for raising ore.*

Left: *A small wrought iron kibble on display at King Edward Mine. These had a rough life passing through narrow shafts and frequently needed replacing.*

Far left: *A rusty and redundant winding steam engine and drum, King Edward Mine.*

The entrance to King Edward Mine Museum.

Looking to the north from here can be seen the bob wall of a pumping engine house at West Wheal Basset, while the view to the west includes the pumping and winding engine houses at Pascoe's Shaft, (678394) with South Condurrow Mine and Wheal Grenville beyond.

Today a restored tin processing plant can be seen at King Edward Mine near Troon (664389) where guided tours are conducted. This was one of the smaller mines on the Great Flat Lode and part of the South Condurrow Mine sett. The workings here were interconnected with those of its larger neighbour, Wheal Grenville, (665386) which had struggled to find copper but met with success with the discovery of the Great Flat Lode. Today the two remaining engine houses are impressive examples of these industrial buildings. When Wheal Grenville closed in 1920 the underground workings of both mines flooded, so only shallow areas of King Edward Mine could be worked. It then operated as the training mine for Camborne School of Mines until 1974. In 1987 a group of volunteers began to conserve the site. Today it also houses part of the Holman Rock Drill Collection.

E. WHEAL PEEVOR, Radnor, near Redruth (706442)

In 2007 this mine was made accessible to the public; a car park was built, ivy stripped from the engine houses and the structures made safe, and a trail of paths laid. It is significant today for it is a surviving example of a site with three engine houses, one for pumping, one for a winching (whim) engine and the other to drive stamps. The ore here was of a particularly high grade, and it formed part of the Great North Down Mines. When copper was no longer viable it successfully transferred to tin production after 1870.

The pumping engine house, more recent concrete foundations, and the side of the whim engine house nearest the camera.

The smaller whim engine house on the east of the sett was constructed in 1872, and subsequently modified to take a larger engine. The capstan base survives, but all other equipment is long gone.

The tall central pumping engine house originally contained a 60 inch engine, later replaced by one of 72 inches. The bob wall is about 1.5 metres thick, typically substantial to take the great weight of the beam. The rare hollow-work or lattice cast-iron beam had been bought from North Downs Mine in 1872 for £540. Wheal Peevor also had the advantage of being near the eastern extremity of the Great County Adit which reached here in about 1793 when it was at a depth of some 100 metres.

Right: *Wheal Peevor's whim engine house, recently restored.*

Far right: *The impressive pumping engine house.*

Below: *The bob wall and grille over the seemingly bottomless shaft.*

Below middle: *The remains of the processing plant below the stamps engine house. Foundations of machinery remain, along with buddles, seen in the foreground.*

Below right: *The stamps engine house, Wheal Peevor.*

The stamps engine house on the western side of the sett cost £223 to build and contained a 32 inch engine. The foundations for the stamps remain; the 48-head set came from Basset & Grylls mine near Wendron in 1876. They were California stamps, so called because they were developed in the gold fields and improved the traditional design.

Below the stamps engine house can be seen the remains of the tin processing plant and buddles. The sett also contains calciners for arsenic removal, although this was not mined here but brought in for treatment. The count house stands by the entrance, but is now a private residence.

Wheal Peevor failed to survive the First World War when explosives, timber and other materials were at a premium, and when many young men went off to fight. Some prospecting was done on the sett during the 1960s - core samples have been found lying on the ground - after which it was forgotten.

At Wheal Rose (716450), about one kilometre north-east of Wheal Peevor, an engine house has been sympathetically converted into domestic accommodation.

F. SERVICE INDUSTRIES

Bickford's Safety Fuse

Gunpowder was used for blasting. Fuses were made by filling hollow goose quills with the black powder, and secured in the holes with clay. However, they proved unpredictable and led to many injuries and fatalities. Then in 1831 William Bickford (1774-1834) invented the safety fuse, a clever idea combining gunpowder and rope that provided a predictable time delay of thirty seconds per foot. He created a machine that could spin the twine around an explosive core, and was additionally waterproofed. Cut into lengths this proved to be much safer, and although more expensive than the old method, was gradually adopted in the mines. To manufacture the fuses he opened a factory at Tuckingmill near Camborne. In 1836 the company opened a manufacturing facility in Simsbury, Connecticut, The Ensign-Bickford Company. Today the factory at Tuckingmill has been turned into industrial units, though a plaque on the wall reminds us of its past.

West Wheal Peevor stamps engine house, with Carn Brea in the background. This mine was unusual in having at one time a steam-driven whim engine operating underground.

Nitroglycerine was tried, but proved to be too unstable. Then in 1866 dynamite, invented by Alfred Nobel, was introduced which contained 80% nitroglycerine but in a safer form.

Holman Brothers
The company was founded in 1801 by Nicholas Holman as a boiler works. Eighty years later his sons, John and James, along with James McCulloch, patented and began to manufacture a new drill, known as the Cornish Rock Drill. This proved very successful, both at home and in foreign mines. Later they diversified into compressors. The company merged with Broom & Wade in 1968 to form CompAir. In 2003 the Camborne part of the operation closed; Holman's No.1 Works is now the site of Tesco while their other site at Camborne is also awaiting redevelopment.

Camborne School of Mines
Formerly based at Trevenson Campus at Pool, it is now part of the University of Exeter and based at the Tremough Campus at Penryn. This institution was founded in 1888 and soon gained international renown. The Camborne School of Mines Museum holds a comprehensive mineral collection.

A length of safety fuse resting on the packet from blasting cartridges.

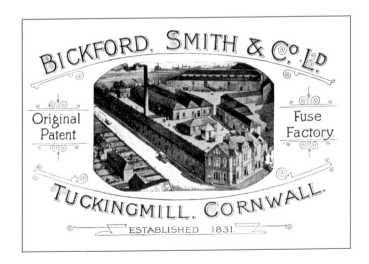

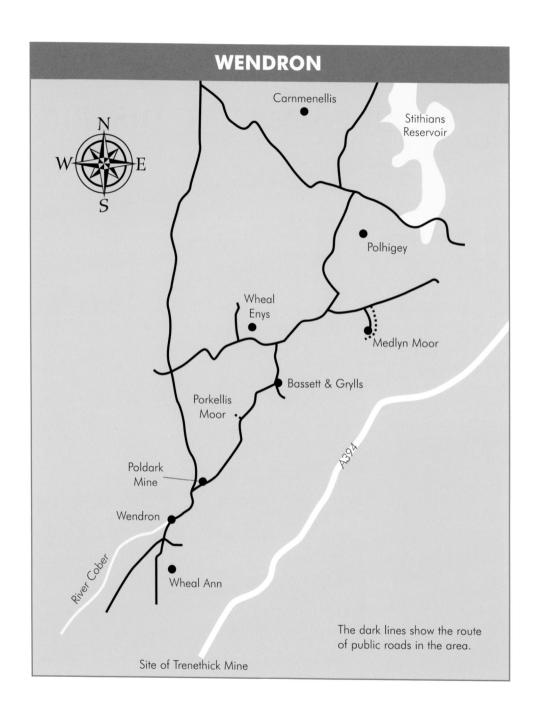

WENDRON

Carnmenellis

Stithians Reservoir

Polhigey

Wheal Enys

Medlyn Moor

Bassett & Grylls

Porkellis Moor

A394

Poldark Mine

Wendron

River Cober

Wheal Ann

The dark lines show the route of public roads in the area.

Site of Trenethick Mine

Chapter 7
THE WENDRON MINING DISTRICT

This stretches up the valley of the River Cober as far as the high ground of Carnmenellis, west of Stithians Reservoir. It was in the floor of the valley that from early times tin streamers originally worked, then chased the lodes in a number of open-cast excavations in the hillsides before resorting to underground mining. The area contains a large but indeterminate number of ancient workings, and by the eighteenth and nineteenth centuries over 70 significant mines were in operation at various times. Noteworthy ones, both within and outside the Nominated Heritage Site include:

Engine houses at Wheal Ann near the village of Wendron now stand in open grazing land.

A. WHEAL ANN (Map 103 - 679303)
Due south of Wendron, and standing in isolation amidst farmland close to the B3297 road to Helston are the engine houses of Wheal Ann. Other remains of mine buildings now provide storage areas for agriculture. It was part of Trumpet Consols, which had the dubious honour of retaining the last wooden beam (or bob) - as opposed to cast iron – which was finally removed in 1889.

B. POLDARK MINE (683315)
The current appellation comes from the central character in Winston Graham's *Poldark* books and television spin-offs. This ancient tin mine was originally Wheal Roots, but was absorbed into Wendron Consols Mine in 1856.

The present Poldark Mine and Activity Centre, established by retired Royal Marine, Peter Young, offers underground tours, family-orientated activities, as well as an interesting museum of Cornish mining. This contains a variety of artefacts, machinery and working models that help illustrate how the mines functioned. One such example is the remains of an early 'rag and chain' pump, universally used to de-water the mines. Rags attached

Poldark Mine.

to a chain were drawn through wooden pipes, and as it was pulled up they raised the water to the surface. The story is brought up to date with the first compressed air rock drill to be used in the county, an exhibit from the museum that was once at Holman Brothers of Camborne, manufacturers of compressed air equipment for the mining industry, and now displayed at Poldark. Similarly, the beam engine now on the site was brought from Greensplatt china clay works near St Austell in 1972-73. This was the last beam engine to work commercially until it was stopped in 1959.

C. PORKELLIS MOOR (688325)

Driving north towards Lower Porkellis, this mine is on the left, and just a short walk along a footpath. The engine house is overgrown and inaccessible, but some of the surface workings remain, including buddles and spoil heaps. These convex domes within a circular pan were used to separate the heavier tin from the waste material by directing a solution of stamped rock via a launder to the centre. Rotating brushes helped the movement of lighter waste material to the circumference, leaving behind the tin concentrate. This was graded as heads, middlings and fines (tails). An operative would disconnect the brushes and remove the material once it had built up sufficiently. This could be further refined in 'keives', or barrels in which the heavier tin would be allowed to sink to the bottom.

The ore was then transported to the nearest smelters where it was moulded into "block-tin". Each smelter had its own tin mark; Harvey's of Hayle, for example, used the Cornish arms of fifteen bezants. From Porkellis Moor it was probably sent to the stannary at Helston, one of five "coinage towns" in Cornwall, the others being Liskeard, Lostwithiel, Truro and Penzance. On the other side of the Tamar Tavistock served the mines of west Devon. At the stannary the tin was assayed for quality by removing a corner from each block. A stannaries mark was applied, and a due paid on it that traditionally went to the Duke of Cornwall. Finally the tin could be sold. The silting up

Surviving buddles at Porkellis Moor, and an ivy-covered chimney stack amongst dense vegetation.

of Helston's harbour during the thirteenth century and the formation of Loe Bar saw Gweek take the town's maritime trade. Dues stopped being levied in 1838, but the past is preserved in the name Coinagehall Street running down to the Cober river.

D. BASSET & GRYLLS MINE (693329)

The restored engine house of this tin mine, formerly known as Porkellis United, can be seen by the side of the road just outside the hamlet of Lower Porkellis. The engine, built by Harvey & Co., along with two boilers, were sold to Rosewarne United near Camborne in 1873 for £1,300, while three years later their 48-head steam stamps were sold to Wheal Peevor near Redruth for £790. In 1858 the sides of a pond at the mine collapsed, flooding the workings and drowning seven miners. Mining was resumed here sporadically in the early twentieth century around Old Men's Shaft.

E. MEDLYN MOOR MINE (706335)

This had the honour of being the last mine still working in the Wendron district following the slump in tin prices, until its 40 inch engine also stopped in 1879. Glimpsed through the trees, and hidden down a lane leading to an animal sanctuary, the remains of a solitary engine house stand in farmland. The chimney stack was usually built into the corner of the building to ease construction and add strength. Like most examples the less substantial lean-to boiler house that once abutted it has gone, leaving odd and apparently random apertures where steam pipes and doorways passed through the thick walls.

A remnant of Basset & Grylls Mine – Tyacke's pumping engine house, named after the mine's purser, can be seen near the road.

Although rusticated today, the outside walls were often whitewashed. The specification for mason's work on an engine and boiler house at Wheal Jane in 1860 stated, '...*pointing and whitewashing Engine House and Boiler House inside and out...*' The contract stipulated that scaffolding would be provided by the mine, although the Taker was responsible for it, while raising the stones, provision of the quoins and providing the workforce was the responsibility of the mason. The work had to be undertaken in accordance with the drawings and directions of the mine's engineers and agents, who would only grant final payment when satisfied with the work. The average engine house, stack and boiler-house was normally erected inside of three months, and there were penalties for failing to complete on time.

Far left: *Medlyn Moor engine house.*

Left: *The tastefully converted stamps engine house at Wheal Enys, Porkellis.*

Anything of worth has been removed over the years, or rotted away, leaving the bare shell exposed to the elements. Machinery, waterwheels, boilers and so on, were often sold when mines stopped and companies closed, and building stone was sold and used elsewhere. One or two families actually specialised in erecting and dismantling engine houses, as well as their engines and equipment, and travelled the mining districts offering their services. For example, the Kinsman family of St Day moved the engine houses at Wheal Peevor to their present locations, while J. C. Lanyon & Son of Redruth dealt in engines and mine equipment, purchased from redundant mines. When the impressive chapel at Porkellis (692334) was built in 1866 to replace an earlier one, dressed stone from an old engine house was used. A short distance down the lane beside the chapel is Wheal Enys, its stamps engine house and adjoining boiler house now converted to residential use (689336). It is therefore of small wonder that so little often remains today of the 3,000 engine houses and beam engines that were once found in Cornwall and West Devon.

F. TRENETHICK WOOD

This very old mine, located south of Wendron, was initially worked for tin, then later copper. It was one of the first mines where, in 1799, Richard Trevithick installed a plunger pole pump, an idea he had developed whereby the pump worked on the down stroke, making it more efficient than the traditional bucket pump. It was also cheaper to produce, not requiring a barrel to be bored, as well as being cheaper to maintain. This was also one of the mines where Trevithick trialled his hydraulic engine, which utilised the power of a column of water rather than steam. Despite being a significant enterprise, it serves as a good example of the large number of relatively small mines that once existed in the Wendron mining district, of which no trace remains today.

G. POLHIGEY MINE (704351)

On the hill overlooking the southern end of Stithians Reservoir is the extensive sett of Polhigey Mine. A very late development took place here in the 1920s, including an electricity generating station, a dressing mill, as well as the last Brunton arsenic calciner constructed in Cornwall. The mill was supplied by a long aerial ropeway. Despite the investment, the enterprise was shortlived, closing around 1930. Now all that remains is Polhigey Terrace, built for the employees, and a few overgrown burrows.

This area around Carnmenellis (698361) is a good example of the mining landscape of much of the region during the nineteenth century. Often the miners kept a parcel of land or a smallholding to augment their incomes. Landowners such as Francis Basset were often prepared to grant them 99-year leases, with a 'three lives' stipulation which said

The houses built for the miners are all that remains of the once extensive Polhigey Mine, and now look out over Stithians Reservoir.

that they would run for a maximum of 99 years or the duration of the lives of three named persons. So, in days of high mortality it was common to name at least one young child. However, the leases were often only available on waste moor land. As this had to be brought into cultivation and would improve the quality of the land it was clearly advantageous to the landlord. It left the patchwork of tiny fields and small miners' cottages that can be seen today.

The area around the village also proved useful for quarrying, an activity that went hand-in-hand with mining, providing materials for the sturdy engine houses and associated buildings.

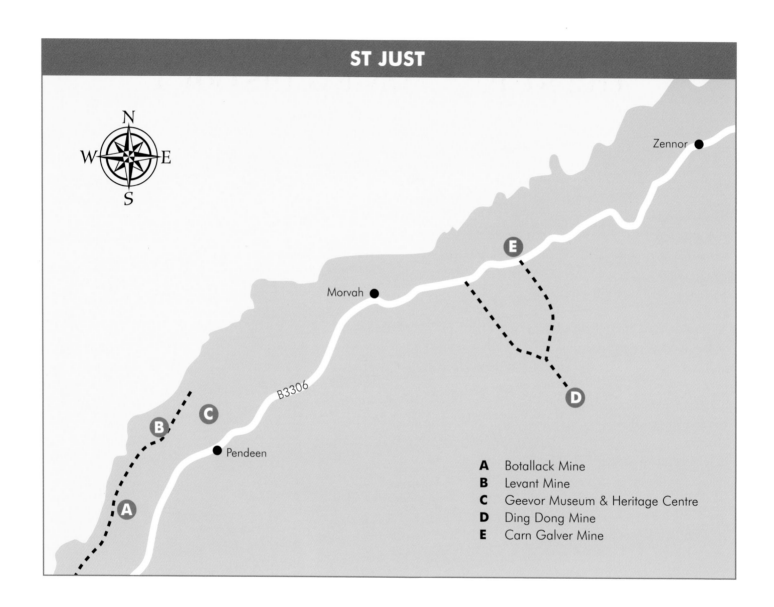

ST JUST

Zennor

E

Morvah

B3306

C

B

Pendeen

A

D

A Botallack Mine
B Levant Mine
C Geevor Museum & Heritage Centre
D Ding Dong Mine
E Carn Galver Mine

Chapter 8
THE ST JUST MINING DISTRICT

At the far west of the region, defying the surging Atlantic Ocean, is the St Just district, including the mining villages of St Just, Botallack and Pendeen.

A. BOTALLACK MINE (Map 102 - 363335)

Famous for the shafts at Crowns section that ran out beneath the sea, the mine was feted with visits by members of the royal family, as well as Victorian writers and tourists. It has often been stated that miners could hear rocks rolling on the sea bed overhead.

The spectacularly located engine houses near the foot of the cliffs are a marvel of engineering: the large cut granite blocks had to be lowered down the cliff, as were the heavy components for the engines themselves. They comprise a pumping house built in 1835, with an unusual internally located chimney stack, and the higher winding house of 1862 with a flue that ran up the cliff to a surviving stack at the cliff-top. The whim operated a tramway in the Boscawen Diagonal Shaft that continued out under the sea to a depth of 192 fathoms. Tragedy struck in 1863 when the chain of the gig carrying miners broke and it careered to the bottom. Eight men and a boy were killed.

Probably the oldest submarine workings were to the north at the Wheal Cock section, with shafts again sunk from the cliff edge during the eighteenth century. Little of this endeavour survives, apart from extensive waste burrows of the old copper floors and capped shafts.

In 1838 the number of people employed at Botallack was 172, a figure that rose to 550 during the 1860s when eleven engines were in use. The extant engine houses are merely the robust survivors of a vast array of ancillary equipment that took up nearly every

Crowns engine houses, possibly the most dramatic situation of any mine.

space, as Wilkie Collins described in *Rambles Beyond Railways* (1850) following a visit to Botallack:

'*Chains, pipes, conduits, protruded in all directions from the precipice; rotten-looking wooden platforms, running over deep chasms, supported great beams of timber and heavy coils of cable; crazy little boarded houses were built, where gulls' nests might have been found in other places.*'

There is some surviving evidence of the dressing floors used during the nineteenth century on the southerly part of the site and either side of the coast path. These include buddles, and above the cliff two rectangular settling tanks where the tin was collected and the water drained off into the sea.

Botallack closed in 1895, but was briefly re-opened before the First World War, and it is from this period that most of the surviving surface structures date.

Arsenic was an important by-product of tin mining. It was used for hardening copper, as a poison, particularly against cotton weevils on the American plantations, as well as to kill Colorado beetles and rats. It also formed the basis of a yellow dye used in the manufacture of wallpaper, and was a constituent of Victorian cosmetics. The finest surviving arsenic refining works in Britain is at Botallack.

A capped shaft of Wheal Cock, just north of Botallack amongst piles of waste on the old copper floors.

Remains of the chambers of the arsenic labyrinth, Botallack, with a more modern headframe beyond.

A restored archway leads into the remains of a Brunton calciner, a giant oven in which 'black tin' was roasted to extract arsenic as a gas. This was fed via a stone flue to the nearby arsenic labyrinth, so called because of its convoluted chambers. The hot arsenic and sulphur gas gradually cooled as it passed through these cold stone-built arched corridors, leaving frost-like deposits on the walls and floor. This was collected into barrels by men with rudimentary protection; a coating of clay over exposed skin and cotton wool in their nostrils. Meanwhile the spent fumes were exhausted up the surviving chimney stack.

Other remains that date from the 1906 re-workings are the tin-dressing mill with the substantial concrete foundations for stamps, while at a lower level circular buddles can be identified.

A restored buddle, used for separating heavy tin particles from the lighter waste. The walls of the 1860's dressing floors can also be seen.

The 1906 mill where tin ore was processed. The tall stack carried away the arsenic fumes from the 'lambreth' or labyrinth, while in the background are the engine houses of Wheal Owles and Wheal Edward.

The conspicuous steel headframe of Allen's Shaft and the nearby chimney stack are from an attempt during the 1980s by Geevor Mine to incorporate some of the old workings.

Southwards along the coast path is West Wheal Owles and its less well preserved neighbour, Wheal Edward. At the former on 11 January 1893 a new tunnel was being blasted when the miners accidentally broke through into the flooded workings of Wheal Drea. Nineteen men and a boy – on his first day underground – were drowned. The mine subsequently closed. Nearby can be found a memorial stone recording the names of the victims. It wasn't the only accident here; on a previous occasion a skip had fallen from the surface down to the 40 fathom sump, yet the sole teenage occupant had survived.

Allen's Shaft headframe and stack from the most recent endeavours of the 1980s.

Botallack beyond West Wheal Owles.

The remains of Wheal Edward on the left, West Wheal Owles on the right, and Botallack beyond.

Behind the engine houses a track follows the course of the old tramway that served these mines, and runs up the hill to Botallack Vean, once part of Penzance School of Mines.

Poorly signposted, and approached down a narrow lane, today Botallack Mine is owned by the National Trust. Information and guide books are available from the restored Count House. Next to it are the remains of the mine's smithy and workshops.

B. LEVANT MINE (368346)

This mine, a short distance up the coast from Botallack, has been owned by the National Trust since 1967. Today the two closely situated and neatly presented engine houses create a false impression of the rough and unruly conglomeration of buildings, tramways and surface workings that were once found here. The larger, roofless engine house was

Botallack Count House, built in 1861-62, now the base for the Area Warden of the National Trust.

Levant Mine.

built in 1835 to house a 40 inch pumping engine built by Harvey & Co. It would only be scrapped in 1934. The smaller Michell's engine house retains its 24-inch whim engine of 1840, also constructed by Harvey & Co. It was re-built in about 1862 following an accident due to human error which resulted in the flywheel going through the roof, but otherwise served reliably for 90 years raising ore in Skip Shaft until the mine's demise in 1930. It is the oldest beam engine remaining in Cornwall, and is run occasionally. The present headframe over the 290 fathom Skip Shaft dates from the 1960s when an electric winding engine was used here by Geevor Mining Company. This engine has recently been restored.

Levant contains extensive surface workings: the remains of the compressor house, built in 1901 to provide compressed air for rock drills, air hoist and other equipment; four arsenic calciners; dressing floors; and the portal of the tramway tunnel that brought ore up the incline to the stamps. These, along with the engine and house that served them, have long since disappeared.

The chimney stack, distinctively banded and with a square base, and the remains of the 1901 compressor house.

One of the most evocative sights is the surviving rectangle of Victorian tiles on the floor of the ruined Count House, as well as fragments of green ceramic tiles where the fireplace once stood. Despite its close proximity to the engine house, smithy and workshops, these hint at the grandeur of the building that was commensurate with the prosperity of the mine. Indeed, in 1890 it was the second largest copper producer in the region after Devon Great Consols.

In 1857 a man engine was installed, operating to a depth of 170 fathoms, later extended to 266 fathoms, and would be the last to work in Cornwall. It was a shame it didn't cease sooner; on 20 October 1919 the linkage between the engine and rod broke. Tragically, 31 men were killed and eleven seriously injured. An investigation discovered a hidden flaw in a wrought-iron plate.

Today there is access to the shaft via the spiral staircase and tunnel that led the miners from The Dry where they changed. The top of the man engine shaft is guarded by a wall and grille.

The tiled floor of the count house. The remains of the fireplace are behind it.

Higher Bal, Levant. The head frame of Guide Shaft once stood beyond the stout granite wall, which incorporates chutes that fed the ore into carts waiting to take it to the stamps.

Geevor Mine. This more recent undertaking gives a suggestion of the conglomeration of buildings and equipment, not to mention waste burrows, that once occupied similar setts.

The steel headframe at Geevor Mine above the main Victory Shaft.

C. GEEVOR MUSEUM AND HERITAGE CENTRE (375345)

This is the largest preserved tin mining site in Europe and only closed as late as 1990. Today it forms a mining heritage museum operated by Pendeen Community Heritage. Near the entrance can be seen the old timber headframe and winding house of Wethered Shaft. Following the road down to the modern mine, the steel headframe above Victory Shaft can be seen, constructed just after the First World War. The surface workings run down the valley towards the sea, and adjoin those of Levant. Settling tanks that formed part of the tin dressing mill can still be seen, as well as roof supports and the concrete plinths of stamps standing amongst a moonscape of rocks and piles of red sand tailings (deposits). Just above the cliffs are remains of earlier nineteenth century water-powered stamps and arsenic calciners.

D. DING DONG MINE (435344)

Travelling north-east along the B3306 towards St Ives, an isolated engine house can be seen on the crest of the hill. This marks the northern edge of the very old Ding Dong Mine. The curious name is of uncertain origin, but it was one of sixteen mines recorded in the area in 1782. In 1796 Richard Trevithick became the mine's engineer. Working with fellow-engineers Edward Bull and William West of Hayle, the remote location was ideal for carry-

The sorry remains of an engine house at Ding Dong Mine, perched high on the heather-covered moors of West Penwith. Despite its remoteness, the mine has an illustrious past.

ing out developments that might infringe Boulton & Watt patents. The first of Trevithick's new whim engines or "puffers" using high-pressure steam and dispensing with a separate condenser was installed here. He also experimented with a windmill that worked too well at this exposed location, forcing the attempt to be abandoned. 'Cap'n Dick' lodged at the nearby village of Madron (454319) when working at Ding Dong.

During the 1840s the mine had five beam engines. It closed in 1877, re-opening briefly between 1911 and 1915. Today the pumping engine house at Greenburrow Shaft can be seen, while others are crumbling ruins. It is approached from a winding footpath over the moors that passes numerous walled shafts overgrown with gorse and heather; taking advantage of its lofty position the mine had nine different adits.

E. CARN GALVER MINE (422365)

A short distance further on, next to a lay-by, are the two ruined engine houses that once formed part of Morvah and Zennor United. In 1872 this mine acquired more advanced pneumatic stamps, powered by a horizontal compound engine as opposed to the normal beam engine. These were faster and more economical to operate. Nearby the count house of the mine now serves as an outdoor activity centre.

Carn Galva engine house; a photograph taken c.1900.

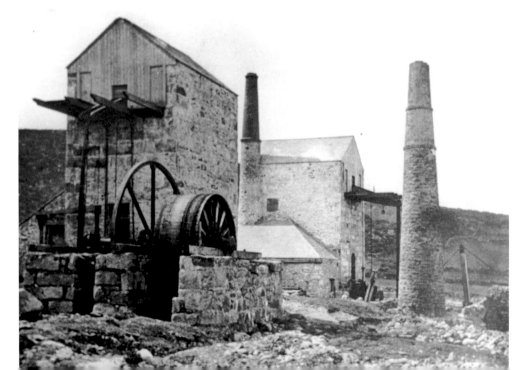

The twin engine houses of Carn Galver Mine. The one on the left contained a whim engine, its neighbour a pumping engine.

A view of Carn Galver and its count house from the path leading to Ding Dong Mine. Heather and bracken-covered burrows fill the middle distance.

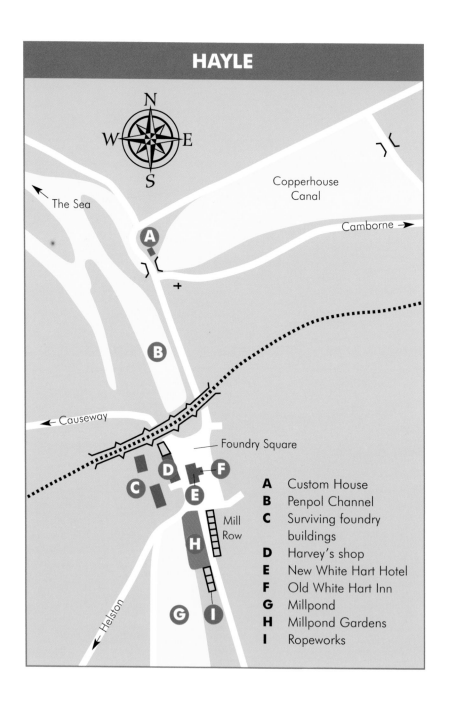

HAYLE

Copperhouse Canal

The Sea

Camborne →

Causeway ←

Foundry Square

Mill Row

Helston

A Custom House
B Penpol Channel
C Surviving foundry
   buildings
D Harvey's shop
E New White Hart Hotel
F Old White Hart Inn
G Millpond
H Millpond Gardens
I Ropeworks

Chapter 9
HAYLE

The port of Hayle contained Copperhouse Foundry and the rival Harvey's Foundry. In fact, through the stature of their buildings and through their employment, the two companies dominated the town and the activities of the community. It was also the centre of significant industrial progress; Trevithick's Cornish boiler, steam rock-drill and other developments began here. A network of railways and tram roads brought ore from the Redruth mines, while ships plied between Hayle and South Wales with ore and coal.

A. COPPERHOUSE

Hayle had the advantage over other Cornish ports of being close to the major mines, and also being on the north coast from where shipments could be sent to South Wales and

Looking across Copperhouse Pool to St. Elwyn's Church, built in 1887-8.

Copperhouse Pool.

The view across Hayle in 1906.

Bristol without going round the treacherous promontory of Land's End. It was for these reasons that the Cornish Copper Company, originally established in Camborne, moved there in 1758. This venture had been established by Sampson Swaine, John Vivian and others to smelt copper locally, rather than sending ore to Swansea. However, they met with concerted opposition from the established Welsh producers, even though they never achieved anything like the output of their rivals who had the advantage of ready coal supplies. Developing the eastern side of the Hayle estuary, then called Ventonleague, they also supplied the nearby mines with coal, timber and iron. Navigation was improved by the construction of a canal enclosed by tidal sluice gates that could be used to flush away the perennial problem of sea-borne sand. In 1789 they expanded onto Carnsew Quay and Cellars. A tidal grist mill producing horse fodder was built in 1842. Later converted to steam power, the 40 foot red brick chimney was only demolished in 1982.

B. HARVEY AND COMPANY

Soon after starting his iron foundry at Carnsew in 1779 John Harvey found himself in contention with his neighbour. To help maintain his independence he deepened the channel of the Penpol River that provided access to his foundry, and acquired his own schooner, the *Providence*. Harvey was soon dealing in a wide range of commodities, from

The Penpol Channel, Hayle.

soap and kettles to pig-iron and coal, in open competition, as well as developing the foundry. In 1795 his firm launched a second vessel, the brig *Henry*, named after his son.

When John Harvey died in 1803 the firm passed to this surviving son. Henry had a third ship built, *Elizabeth*. In 1815 a new ship, *Fame*, joined the Harvey fleet. He was also able to help provide his brother-in-law, Richard Trevithick, with castings when he was developing high-pressure steam engines, his Cornish boiler and plunger-pole pump, as well as his road locomotive of 1801.

Becoming one of the adventurers in the re-working of Wheal Vor led Henry to set up a tin-smelter at Foundry Square in 1816 (Map 102 - 558372). This also processed tin from other mines in the area and he soon acquired shares in Binner Downs Mine. However, his operation was short-lived, for Wheal Vor took over the Cornish Copper Company's tin smelting plant in 1819, while the C. C. C. started their own iron foundry, in competition with Harvey's.

Buildings once used for pattern-making.

The millpond served as the foundry's reservoir.

This was not the only cause of rancour; there were squabbles over boundaries that even led to the two workforces brawling. Frustrating his rival, in 1818/19 Harvey again widened the contentious Penpol River channel and had a new quay built at Carnsew. This major development, being 400 metres long, can still be seen today. The renowned Cornish engineer Arthur Woolf (1766-1837) was actively involved in helping him develop the foundry, aiding in the procurement of new machinery to increase the capacity of the works. Today Millpond Gardens is the site of the hammer mill, boring mill and corn mill. (557369). The adjoining pond provided power for the machinery. The Harvey premises also contained a timber-yard and three grist-mills producing fodder-North, South and Front Mills - as well as lime kilns.

To supply the mines as well as ships there was also a ropewalk. Hemp from Russia, and later manila and sisal from South America and the Far East, along with tar and linseed oil for rope making, often came by sea from London and Liverpool. The roofless remains of the rope works survives behind Millpond Gardens, containing clearly defined rooms

The remains of the boring-mill.

The ropeworks. On the right is the manila, hemp and sisal bale store; on the left, the start of the rope walk.

Right: *The ropeworks.*

Middle right: *Basic rope-making equipment as used on a rope walk. As the large central gearwheel is turned, the rope, looped round the four hooks, is twisted. The machine is slowly moved back on its wheels as the rope is formed. This example, now fitted with a Perspex guard, is at Morwellham.*

Far right: *Twisted rope, two-core on the left, four-core on the right.*

  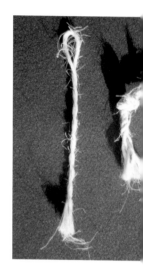

for storing the materials, a machine shop and processing area, engine room, boiler room as well as the ropewalk. The capstan pit can be identified, as well as the base for the horizontal steam engine.

Harvey's also had a bake house to produce bread for local consumption. The Foundry Farm provided much of the grain, as well as oats for the company's horses and oxen. The White Hart inn would also be established in Foundry Square.

When *Elizabeth* was wrecked in 1819-20 it was replaced with the *John Adams*. Sadly this vessel was lost in bad weather in 1823 with all hands. In 1827 Henry Harvey bought the brig *Rosewarne* for £900. Five years later he acquired the brig *Phoebe*, primarily for importing timber from North America. It also marked a turning point as the company became shipwrights. Between 1834 and 1844 thirteen vessels were built at Hayle and would serve the business. Return cargoes included coal, pig-iron and wrought-iron, boiler-plates and sheet-iron, while salt was carried for the Cornish pilchard industry.

South-east of Hayle was Wheal Alfred, mainly a copper mine and named after Alfred Jenkin, the mineral agent of the Duke of Buckingham. It was worked on and off over the years, and with various degrees of success, generating huge profits as well as spectacular losses. In 1824 manager John Taylor used it to conduct trials between Arthur Woolf's compound engine coupled with boilers of Woolf's design, both built by Harvey's, and a traditional single-cylinder machine using Trevithick's Cornish boilers. The latter triumphed.

A change of direction for Harvey's came in 1831 when a shop was opened selling everyday household goods. Meanwhile the foundry was producing a vast range of articles, from agricultural equipment to domestic ranges – even the galley kitchen of Brunel's *Great Western*.

At about the same time the Hayle causeway was built, greatly aiding communications with Penzance, and in 1833 Hayle was made a Stannary town, with the coinage hall conveniently located on the Harvey Foundry premises. The Duchy's levy would end five years later. In 1834 Henry wrote, "*…had it not been for our exertions at Hayle many of the mines in the County would have ceased from working several years since.*"

The White Hart Hotel, Foundry Square, built in 1838 to replace the small building on the left, now the Masonic Hall, that was the original White Hart inn run by Richard Trevithick's wife, Jane, nee Harvey.

A 13 inch dolphin-handle siege mortar weighing 5 tons and cast at Harvey's in 1856 for use in the Crimean War. It now stands beside Carnsew Road.

Harvey's shop and offices, Foundry Square.

Not that their work was confined to Cornwall; Harvey's gained a Dutch contract for steam engines to drain the Haarlemmer Meer, a task completed by 1852 using the largest steam pumping engines ever produced, as well as providing pumping engines for London waterworks and the Severn Tunnel project to counter the inundations cause by the Great Spring. In 1846 the iron-hulled steam tug *Prussian Eagle* was constructed for use on the River Rhone, and would be the first of a number of iron ships built at Hayle. This was aided in 1888 by the construction of a new slipway, providing the capacity for even larger ships, including the cargo steamer *Ramleh* launched in 1891, which at almost 4,000 tons would be the largest vessel built in Cornwall.

The Custom House, built by the Cornish Copper Company in 1862.

Meanwhile, in 1862 Hayle finally gained its own custom house. Five years later, during the severe mining recession, Harvey's acquired significant property from Sandys, Carne, and Vivian – formerly the Cornwall Copper Company – giving them control of the port. In 1875 the remains of the rival company was acquired by them. The sale included some 140 dwelling houses and cottages in the town.

Evidence today of the Cornwall Copper Company includes the *scoria* or copper slag used for building blocks that can be seen in some of the buildings, as well as Copperhouse Canal and Pool.

By the end of the nineteenth century Harvey's foundry too was struggling to turn a profit, being largely supported by the commercial side of the business. In 1903 the foundry's machinery and tools were sold, and the company re-organised as merchants, leaving engineers operating a repair shop. The London office was also closed, though the South African branch that had begun with an agency in 1886 continued until 1914.

C. HAYLE RAILWAY

In 1837 the railway from Hayle to Redruth was completed, designed from the outset to use locomotives on a standard gauge track. It commenced at Hayle Foundry and originally had inclined planes at Angarrack and Penponds. A stationary engine on 'Steamer's Hill' hauled up the wagons using cables, then they were pulled by locomotives. When the line was extended from Truro to Penzance with the construction of the West Cornwall Railway, opened in 1853, the inclines were bypassed by viaducts, initially of timber and designed by I. K. Brunel, along with one traversing Foundry Square. The line fell under the control of the Great Western Railway in 1876.

D. SERVICE INDUSTRIES

Other businesses in the town included a brewery, established in 1815 by the Ellis family, J & F Pool providing mining equipment, and Loggan's Mill (575385). The National Explosives Company was established in 1888 on a suitably remote site at Upton Towans. These buildings were demolished in the 1920s.

E. RECENT HISTORY

The town of Hayle we see today is the product of its industrial past, even if many of the buildings that played such an important part in its development have disappeared. As early as 1908 Sir Compton Mackenzie, in *My Life and Times*, said that Hayle had become a small industrial town living in its past.

Recent attention has focussed on the refurbishment of Foundry Square, and the regeneration of some of the historic buildings under Hayle Townscape Heritage Initiative. These have received Objective One funding, with £1.9 million spent on Foundry Square buildings, creating workshops, visitor facilities and offices, while the former White's Warehouse has become home to Nixon's, complete with conference facilities and a new restaurant, though a far cry from John Harvey's vision of the site.

Loggan's Mill, undergoing restoration in 2008. The plaque on the wall reads W H 1852.

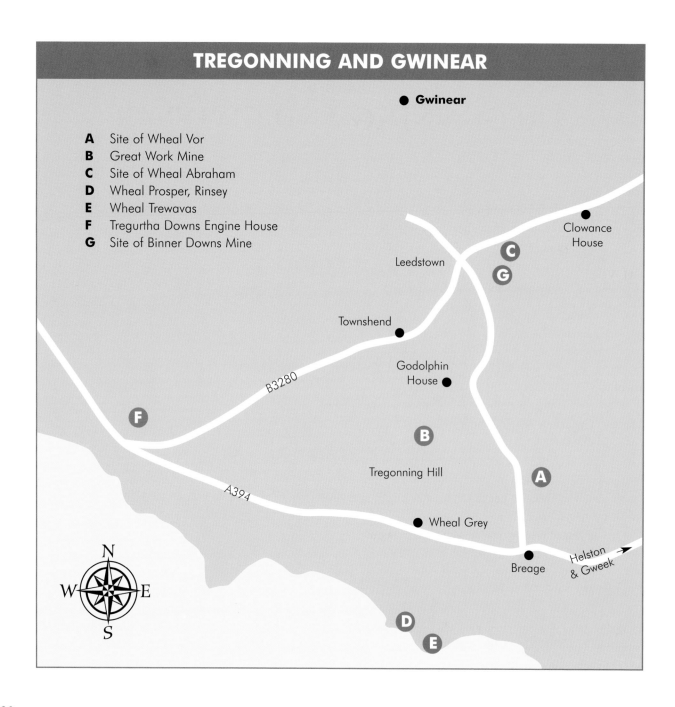

TREGONNING AND GWINEAR

● **Gwinear**

A   Site of Wheal Vor
B   Great Work Mine
C   Site of Wheal Abraham
D   Wheal Prosper, Rinsey
E   Wheal Trewavas
F   Tregurtha Downs Engine House
G   Site of Binner Downs Mine

● Clowance House

C

Leedstown

G

Townshend ●

Godolphin House ●

B

B3280

F

Tregonning Hill

A394

A

● Wheal Grey

● Breage

Helston & Gweek →

D

E

N
W E
S

Chapter 10
TREGONNING AND GWINEAR

The Godolphin mining district stretched along the coast from Marazion to Porthleven, and inland to the village of Gwinear.

A. WHEAL VOR, north of Breage
Amazingly, today little evidence remains of these once extensive workings, apart from the odd chimney stack, spoil heap or engine house.

This tin mine dates from at least as early as the fifteenth century, and was possibly one of the few mines supplied with Thomas Savery's steam-driven pumping engine in the early years of the eighteenth century. It could also claim to be the first place gunpowder was used in a mine. It was certainly the richest mine in Cornwall at one time, though this didn't guarantee its survival in this precarious industry.

In 1814 it was re-opened by the Gundry brothers, supported by fellow-adventurers, including Henry Harvey of Hayle. The mine used an engine provided by the engineer Arthur Woolf which was said to use much less coal than ones built by Boulton and Watt. It was probably here too that steam was first used to successfully drive stamps developed by Woolf. One of the engine houses containing a 50 inch Woolf engine burnt down in 1839. The mine's adventurers also took over the Cornish Copper Company's smelting plant in 1823 in order to refine the tin, and this was later moved to the mine where it operated until 1844.

The mine again closed for a period, and when re-opened a new engine of huge proportions was built by Harvey & Co., still shareholders in the mine, to de-water it. It was estimated that over 706 million gallons of water had to be removed. When this new 100 inch

An impressive engine house, one of the few remaining pieces of evidence of the once extensive sett of Wheal Vor.

engine – the most powerful built in Cornwall – was started in 1854 the event was celebrated with brass bands and a firework display enjoyed by a large crowd. Two years later a man-engine was installed, reported at the time to save a quarter of the labour costs, though no doubt the miners also appreciated the labour-saving device. It was one of only four in the county in 1860, a number that rose to 16 by 1865. To drive the stamps the mine required seven reservoirs with a capacity of over 3.5 million gallons of water.

Wheal Vor was again in trouble in 1860. The 100 inch engine, along with another Harvey one of 85 inches, were using an unsustainable 600 tons of coal a month, so both were stopped and subsequently sold.

B. GREAT WORK MINE, near Breage (Map 102 - 596308)
The surviving Leeds Shaft pumping engine house and stack, owned by the National Trust, gives us a glimpse of what was once, as its name suggests, a significant mine. The whim engine house, stamps engine house, count house, stables, calciner, blacksmiths' and carpenters' shops are long gone. Yet it has an interesting past; it was here that in 1689 Thomas Epsley is said to have demonstrated the advantage of gunpowder to the Godolphins, leading to its introduction in their mines. During the eighteenth century Newcomen engines were used here, and during the 1850s a 40 inch engine built by Harvey & Co. that was designed to work at 60 lbs. pressure, possibly the highest rate used, and 20 lbs. more than required by the average steam engine at that time.

There was a doomed attempt to re-open the mine during the 1930s. The stamps were blown up in the 1960s, a fate that sadly befell many engine houses and concomitant substantial machine beds. The surviving stack - like an upended telescope - is unusual, being in three stages with the top two of brick.

C. WHEAL ABRAHAM
The engines and boilers required large quantities of water for producing steam and running their condensers, and this was usually retained in large ponds close to the mines. Fresh water was usually required, as that raised from the mine was often very corrosive. In 1806 at Wheal Abraham, Horsedowns, (Map 104 - 615343) to the east of Leedstown, one such pond burst its banks following heavy rain, and the water poured into the mine, overwhelming the pumps and adits. Some 40 miners were trapped below

ground but managed to reach safety, whilst about seven were not so lucky. (In a similar incident forty years later at East Wheal Rose, St Newlyn East, 39 men died and just four were rescued as a result of flooding following a thunderstorm.)

Little of the Wheal Abraham workings remain today.

D. WHEAL PROSPER, RINSEY (Map 102 - 594270)

On the cliffs above the holiday makers' hideaway of Rinsey Cove stands this solitary engine house, constructed in 1860, that was once part of the Marazion Mines group. The mine closed in 1865, but the engine house survived and was restored by the National Trust in 1970-71. Unsurprisingly, it was not the only mine to be named Wheal Prosper…

Wheal Prosper, Rinsey, had a short working life.

Wheal Prosper.

Wheal Trewavas in an impressive location part-way down the cliffs in an area now owned by the National Trust.

E. WHEAL TREWAVAS (Map 102 - 597265)

Further east along the coastal footpath is the spectacularly located Wheal Trewavas, where two engine houses are perched halfway down the cliffs. One housed a 45 inch pumping engine, later upgraded to a 70 inch, a task that can only be marvelled at in such a perilous and relatively remote location. A terraced platform constructed next to the westerly engine house provided a little more space and once contained a capstan. Shafts from the mine ran out beneath the sea, but once flooded sealed the fate of the enterprise.

Today, from the footpath one can admire the beautifully constructed chimney stacks, their pointing scoured away, that utilised remarkably small pieces of stone gleaned locally. On the cliff top to the west there remains evidence of worked-over ground, partly overgrown with purple heather.

F. TREGURTHA DOWNS ENGINE HOUSE West of Goldsithney (Map 102 - 537311)

The engine house was constructed with unusual slit windows so as not to diminish the strength of the building, yet it was gutted by fire in 1889. Despite this, Harvey & Co. who had also acquired the mine, managed to rebuild the engine, and the building was restored. Although now a private residence, it is noteworthy for this significant 80-inch engine that it once housed. It was first built for Alfred Consols near Hayle in 1854 by Copperhouse Foundry, then after ten years was installed at Crenver & Wheal Abraham United, near Leedstown. This mine closed in 1876, and after remaining idle for six years it was transferred to Owen Vean & Tregurtha Downs Mines. The 40-ton bob was transported on a wagon drawn by 45 horses, followed by a large crowd, many curious to see if Relubbus Bridge would withstand the weight! Then when this operation ceased it was removed to South Crofty in 1903 where it continued to provide reliable service until 1955, having the honour of being the last Cornish engine remaining working in a Cornish mine.

The engine house at Tregurtha Downs with its narrow windows has been turned into a private residence.

Today the engine house can be glimpsed through the trees from the Goldsithney road, with a closer view afforded by a footpath.

G. BINNER DOWNS

This copper mine flourished in the early years of the eighteenth century. Even in 1838 it had four pumping engines and two whims, but no water wheels due to the lack of

136

surface water. At that time 390 people were employed and the mine produced 2,704 tons of ore. Henry Harvey of Hayle was a shareholder in the mine, and it was also here that experiments were conducted with 'superheated steam' which was re-used, a concept investigated by Richard Trevithick on his return from Peru. Again, the land has been returned to agriculture and nothing of note survives.

H. MINING COMMUNITIES

Much of the land in the area was in the hands of prominent families. Near Praze-an-Beeble, the Clowance estate, extending to some 2,430 hectares, was owned by the St Aubyn family (Map 104 - 635351). The village itself, with its long main street and delightful chapel, commemorates this with the St Aubyn's Arms at the bottom of the hill (Map 104 - 636356). The Godolphins, with their seat at Godolphin House, (Map 102 - 601317) were also major landowners in the area and prospered from the mines. The manor house, now owned by the National Trust, dates from the fifteenth century. Nearby the village of Godolphin Cross provided tenanted properties for miners and farm workers.

Sober and austere Godolphin House.

Leedstown, (Map 102 - 604344) owned by the Duke of Leeds, the last surviving heirs of the Godolphins, had developed to cater for the local mines. The parish of Crowan, of which the village was a part, contained twelve mines in 1835, and soon chapels, shops, an inn and school were built.

To the south, Townshend (Map 102 - 593329) was named after a descendant of the Duke of Leeds. Here the River Hayle was used to power Gilbert Stamps as well as a corn mill. Again, a thriving community grew up with similar amenities, including a Methodist chapel and Sunday school.

The origin of Leedstown is preserved in the village pub.

Gwinear (Map 102 - 595374) had many mines nearby, including the ancient copper mines of Relistian, Herland and Wheal Alfred. The church bells were rung and a ball was held in 1851 to celebrate the erection of a new engine house. Roseworthy Hammer Mills, established in 1790, was also located here using water from a stream to drive its equipment via two waterwheels, making mining equipment from boilers to shovels. It was run by the Tuckingmill Foundry Co., and J. & F. Pool of Hayle, before closing in 1939. The works was subsequently demolished.

Porthleven harbour c.1900.

Gweek, at the highest navigable point of the Helford River, was for some time the de facto harbour of Helston. Streams flowing into the creek had been streamed for tin since the Bronze Age, while the oak trees on the river banks were coppiced for charcoal to augment that which was imported. During the nineteenth century the wharves and a saw mill were stacked with timber from Norway, while coal was also brought in for the mines. The coal yard in this sleepy little village is now used by marine drilling and civil engineering contractors, Seacore, the timber yards changed to boat yards.

Porthleven Harbour was originally constructed between 1811 and 1818 by a group of London merchants to afford refuge for shipping. However, it was not very successful other than as a fishing port until taken over in 1855 by Harvey & Co. to provide a facility closer to the mines at a time when Gweek was silting up. They invested in a breakwater and lock gates to create a closed dock that was no longer dependent on the tides, as well as sluices to flush silt from the outer harbour. The port was then used to bring in materials for the local mines, as well as limestone, fertilisers and fodder. China clay from Wheal Grey pit was shipped from Porthleven, the 'white gold' that would eventually supplant the county's hard-rock mining having been discovered by William Cookworthy at nearby Tregonning Hill.

Harvey's retained the harbour until 1961. There were also several boatbuilding yards in the village, but despite gaining an enviable reputation none survive today.

Evidence from various periods remain at Geevor Mine, from nineteenth century spoil heaps, the remains of 1920's stamps, and the late-twentieth century mine buildings.

Chapter 11
CHANGING FORTUNES

Following the prosperous years of the 1850s the next two decades saw the mining industry go into sharp decline. Better quality and more cheaply produced ores were being produced abroad, Cornish reserves were getting harder to reach, whilst a lack of investment was often revealed by aging equipment. Whereas copper was fetching £115 a ton in 1860, by the end of the decade it had dropped to £80. Only the more prosperous mines survived, and even this often meant looking for tin which enjoyed a short-lived boom during the early 1870s, or temporarily closing when mineral prices dropped.

Faced with poverty, many thousands of Cornish families emigrated to find work in the mines of North America and Australia, while some made the grudging transition to the collieries of the north or the china clay pits of mid-Cornwall. Escape was actively encouraged by emigration commissioners who toured the mining districts, offering cheap passages and a promise of a better life. Cornish communities of 'Cousin Jacks' were soon found 'wherever there was a hole in the ground'. Today many still carry on the traditions of their old homeland.

The less fit or adventurous found their once thriving mining communities hit by hard times, with allied trades struggling to survive, cottages deserted, while the mines them-selves were stripped of valuable equipment, an unsentimental process that had occurred even in the good times when a mine closed or contracted.

In the first two decades of the twentieth century attempts were made to re-open some of the more promising mines, and it is from these later endeavours that the best preserved remains can be seen today, such as at Botallack. It is those places that have continued to be used and have adapted over the years, such as Charlestown or Geevor, that now provide the most comprehensive views of our mining heritage.

One of the overwhelming impressions gained whilst researching this book is how thoroughly nature has reclaimed most of the mining landscape. Areas that were once covered in an unsightly conglomeration of activities associated with mineral extraction often reveal nothing of their past. This has come about through a combination of factors; the stripping of anything of value, either to be used elsewhere or for scrap, the action of the often severe weather and the prolific plant growth of invasive species such as ivy and heather.

Gaining World Heritage status in 2006 has had a positive effect on former industrial sites, raising awareness of them and fostering an appreciation of their historical importance. For example, the long forgotten triumvirate of engine houses at Prince of Wales Mine near Harrowbarrow won grants of £180,000 for conservation work. Similarly, in July 2007 the *Western Morning News* reported that plans were revised for the former Holman's No.3 Rock Drill Works in Camborne when '*structures not previously considered to be of any particular value were shown to be important to the understanding of the site's history, which prompted the redesign.*' As well as a reduced number of flats and houses, provision was also made for an interpretation centre and a home for a replica of Trevithick's 1801 road locomotive, the Puffing Devil.

Such investment will be vindicated by public patronage. As we have seen, there are a diverse range of sites offering a variety of experiences, from organised underground tours and traditional museums, to walks and cycle trails. It is hoped that this book has inspired and encouraged readers to explore some of our rich mining heritage in Cornwall and West Devon.

GLOSSARY

Adit – a nearly horizontal shaft to drain mine workings.

Adventurers - speculators who developed new mines.

Bal – Cornish for mine.

Bal maiden – female mine workers engaged in surface work.

Consols or **Consolidated** – a group of mines working as one company.

Count House – (Accounts House) – a mine's office and administrative centre.

Deads – waste material containing no ore, usually dumped near mines.

Dressing – separating the ore from the worthless waste material.

Kibble – a wrought-iron bucket used to bring ore to the surface.

Lode – a deposit of metallic ore held in the surrounding rock.

Man-engine – a mechanical lift for miners.

Pair – A group of miners who worked as a team, though not necessarily in twos.

Stamps – machine for crushing ore.

Sett – the land area encompassing an individual mine.

Ticketing – a method of selling ore, when smelters' agents attached to samples of ore tickets stating the price they were willing to pay.

Tributer – a miner paid according to the value of the ore brought to the surface.

Truck system – the use of tokens as payment in mines, redeemed at the mines themselves.

Tut-worker – a miner paid according to how much a fathom was worked.

Wheal – Cornish name for a mine.

Whim – a winch, initially powered by a horse or mule, used to raise or lower materials or men.